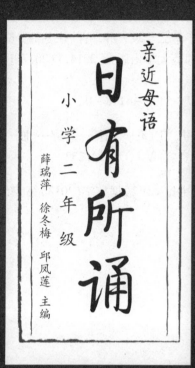

亲近母语

日有所诵

小学二年级

薛瑞萍 徐冬梅 邱凤莲 主编

第四版

广西师范大学出版社
·桂林·

图书在版编目(CIP)数据

日有所诵. 小学二年级／薛瑞萍,徐冬梅,邱凤莲 主编.
—桂林:广西师范大学出版社,2014.1(2017.1 重印)
(亲近母语)
ISBN 978 – 7 – 5495 – 4198 – 0

Ⅰ.①日… Ⅱ.①薛… ②徐… ③邱… Ⅲ.①阅读课 – 小
学 – 教学参考资料 Ⅳ.①G624.233

中国版本图书馆 CIP 数据核字(2013)第 175438 号

出 品 人:刘广汉
责任编辑:刘美文　卢　义
装帧设计:徐　妙

广西师范大学出版社出版发行

(广西桂林市中华路22号　　　邮政编码:541001)
(网址:http://www.bbtpress.com)

出版人:张艺兵
全国新华书店经销
销售热线: 021 – 31260822 – 882/883
山东临沂新华印刷物流集团印刷
(山东省临沂市高新技术开发区新华路东段　邮政编码:276017)
开本:890mm×1 240mm　　1/32
印张:6.875　　　　　字数:190 千字
2014 年 1 月第 1 版　　2017 年 1 月第 7 次印刷
定价:16.80 元

如发现印装质量问题,影响阅读,请与印刷厂联系调换。

亲近母语

亲近母语研究院

【丛书主编】

薛瑞萍　徐冬梅　邱凤莲

【本册主编】

丁云

【编　委】（按姓氏笔画排序）

丁云　丁筱青　丁慈矿　王永燕

余耀　邱凤莲　邵龙霞　张建军

岳乃红　徐冬梅　薛瑞萍

琅琅书声　朗朗乾坤

——写给老师和爸爸妈妈的话

诵读就是深层阅读。日不间断的记诵，就是炼心的过程。水滴石穿，绳锯木断，天长日久，积累的是语言，培养的是诗性，也是定力和静气。

光有智商是靠不住的。什么叫智慧，就是对应当做和必须做的事情专心致志。诵读就是炼心，就是修戒定慧，就是培养聚精会神的能力。当他聚精会神，他便融入对象，吸取对象，成为对象。就这样兴趣盎然地一路诵下，或早或迟，或深或浅，所读所诵，都将内化为他的精神气质。

借着诵读，反复作用于儿童眼睛、耳朵、大脑、心灵的是什么？

是语言。

新鲜丰富的语言就是滋养大脑和心灵的新鲜丰富的营养，仅仅是日常生活语言是远远不能满足儿童对于母语的需要的——怎么办？大手小手同捧一本书，和孩子一起读起来、诵起来。

诵读的材料一定要是和儿童生活、儿童趣味密切相关的。最初的诵读，一定要是"有我的诵读"。这样的诵读，是对儿童的呵护，也是对生命的尊重。对于儿童来说，比起背了多少，背了多深更重要的，是他们这样做的时候是否快乐，是否因此更爱自己，更爱这个世界。

儿童是成人之父，儿童是世界的希望。

对于儿童的精神发展而言，提供健康美好的母语的营养，用琅琅书声为他们构筑一个温馨、实在的成长环境，既是强健儿童的骨骼，也是丰满他们的血肉。既是给他们打造坚固的船体，也是为他们扬起漂亮的风帆。

琅琅书声，朗朗乾坤。

让我们期待，让我们行动。

薛瑞萍

出版说明

《日有所诵》推出第四次修订版了。这是亲近母语研究院历经十年研究，五年编写，四次修订的倾心之作。自 2007 年正式出版以来，这套读物走进了很多教室、很多家庭，诵读成为孩子们每天的生活，成为一个个家庭幸福的时光。这套书也因此成为儿童诵读教材中的领跑品牌。

作为一套为孩子们量身定做的儿童诵读教材，与其他一些诵读教材相比，它具有以下特色：

1. 经典性：这是这套儿童诵读教材最基本的特点。编者在广泛选材的基础上，进行了一次次精心遴选。被选入的作品都是符合儿童心性的、经典的诗性文本。文本体裁丰富多样，有儿歌、童谣、现当代诗歌、古诗词曲、晨读对韵等等。同时，也精选了《论语》、《孟子》、《老子》、古代寓言、古代散文中易于儿童记诵和接受的章节。

2. 课程化：这套儿童诵读教材根据各个年龄段孩子的阅读能力有序地安排了诵读内容，努力让孩子读到他们真正该读并且适合读的东西。为了方便学生使用，我们将每学年分为一册，每册分为上下两卷，每卷 16 个单元，以对应每个学期中的 16 周次。每周安排了五篇作品，其中重点推荐两篇。每册后面的附录部分，基本为国学经典启蒙，供学有余力的孩子诵读。

3. 儿童本位：为了让孩子喜读、乐读，所选文本从儿童心性出发，充分择选音韵和谐、朗朗上口、能打开儿童心灵、启迪儿童灵性的作品。同时将各题材作品有序地安排到各个单元，让孩子在每个单元中接触到不同风格、不同个性的作品。

本次出版，我们精心组织了修订工作，在保持该书原有风格特色的基础上,进一步吸收了各方在使用过程中提出的一些较好的建议和意见,对各册体裁分布和内容选择的梯度做了微调。如古诗内容,仍坚持以唐诗为主,同时增选了一部分适合孩子诵读的其他朝代的优秀诗歌,删除了一部分内容与孩子相去较远、不大能够与孩子内心产生呼应的篇章。其分布方式也由原来按照体裁、年代排列,改为按照难易程度编排。除此之外,将童谣的诵读一直延续到二年级下卷,将儿童诗的诵读按不同程度分布到各个级段等等,整体上力求更加贴近孩子,更加方便家庭和学校的使用。

怎样引导孩子"日有所诵",仍是很多家长和老师关心的问题,在此,作如下几点提醒:

1. 持之以恒:引导孩子"日有所诵"当然应该做到每日诵读,只有"持之以恒",才能使"习惯成自然",才能使孩子不觉得诵读是额外的负担。但是,每日诵读,并不一定要求每天诵读新的篇章,温故而知新,诵读也需要不断复习。

2. 熟读成诵:用各种形式的读来加强孩子的记忆,同时培养孩子的语言感受能力,可以水到渠成、熟读成诵。但对于有些稍长或不便于记忆的篇目,如儿童诗、现代诗、中外散文选篇等,可以让孩子熟读,不一定要求背诵。

3. 适当指导:教师和家长的适当指导有助于提升孩子"日有所诵"的兴趣和效果。教师和家长可以参照书中的赏析(每周两篇)和注释,为孩子提供一些指导。但是孩子对作品只要大致理解、粗知大义即可,不必字字都落实。

特别需要指出的是,各个家庭、班级、孩子的情况不同,不能强求整齐划一,不能强求每个孩子每篇都要记诵,家长、老师要根据具体情况,确定不同的使用方法。为了不加重孩子的负担,可以每周给孩子选择一首(篇)或者两三首(篇)背诵,其余熟读即可。即使一篇不背诵,儿童在日积月累的诵读过程中,也会获得很大的收益。

我们期望孩子通过日有所诵,丰厚底蕴、形成语感,从而带动更广泛的阅读;我们期望通过儿童阅读,让更多的孩子亲近母语,亲近世界的优秀文化;我们更期望通过优质的阅读和母语教育,让更多的孩子走向优秀、走向更加幸福的人生!

编　者

目　录·【上卷】

1

【下 卷】

3

上
卷

第一单元

wǒ de mǎ er zhēn zhèng qiǎo
我 的 马 儿 真 正 巧

yì míng
◎ 佚 名

wǒ de mǎ er zhēn zhèng qiǎo
我的马儿真正巧,

wǒ de mǎ er bù chī cǎo
我的马儿不吃草,

dē er jià
嘚儿,驾!

mǎ er pǎo de kuài
马儿跑得快,

mǎ er pǎo de hǎo
马儿跑得好,

dǐ dǐ dē dē
底底嘚嘚!

dǐ dǐ dē dē
底底嘚嘚!

mǎ er zhēn huì pǎo
马儿真会跑。

大象

[苏联] 马尔夏克

小朋友送给大象一双鞋。

大象接过鞋子一瞅说：

我穿的鞋要又宽又大，

并且，一双 不够，得四只！

（韦苇 译）

插 秧
chā yāng

zhōng guó tái wān zhān bīng
（中 国 台 湾 ）詹 冰

shuǐ tián shì jìng zi
水 田 是 镜 子

zhào yìng zhe lán tiān
照 映 着 蓝 天

zhào yìng zhe bái yún
照 映 着 白 云

zhào yìng zhe qīng shān
照 映 着 青 山

zhào yìng zhe lǜ shù
照 映 着 绿 树

nóng fū zài chā yāng
农 夫 在 插 秧

chā zài lǜ shù shang
插 在 绿 树 上

chā zài qīng shān shang
插 在 青 山 上

chā zài bái yún shang
插 在 白 云 上

chā zài lán tiān shang
插 在 蓝 天 上

赏析　第一节从远写到近，第二节从近写到远，越写越新，越写越奇，这种新奇的手法，都来自"水田是镜子"的奇妙想象。特别是文中语言的不断反复，不断递进，更增添了诗歌的意趣。

yún
云

zhōng guó tái wān   yú yǎn kūn
（中 国 台 湾）于 衍 锟

yún shì
云是

zǒu dòng de xié zi
走 动 的 鞋 子。

zǒu guo gāo shān
走 过 高 山，

zǒu guo dà hǎi
走 过 大 海，

zǒu guo hěn duō dì fang
走 过 很 多 地 方。

qīng piāo piāo de xié zi
轻 飘 飘 的 鞋 子，

zǒu guo de lù
走 过 的 路，

yì diǎn hén jì   yě méi yǒu
一 点 痕 迹 也 没 有。

赏析

云是什么？棉花糖、小绵羊……每个小朋友都有自己的想法。而作者想到的是会走动的鞋子，更有趣的是，这鞋子走过的路，一点痕迹也没有，仔细想一想，这个想法还真是奇妙。

xún hú yǐn jūn
寻 胡 隐 君 ①

míng gāo qǐ
（明）高 启

dù shuǐ fù dù shuǐ
渡 水 复 渡 水 ②，

kàn huā hái kàn huā
看 花 还 看 花 。

chūn fēng jiāng shàng lù
春 风 江 上 路，

bù jué dào jūn jiā
不 觉 到 君 家 。

注释
① 寻：访问。胡隐君：一位姓胡的隐士。
② 复：又。

第二单元

dà jiā lǒng lái zuò bǎ xì
大 家 拢 来 做 把 戏

mín jiān tóng yáo
◎ 民 间 童 谣

xiǎo gē ge xiǎo dì di
小 哥 哥，小 弟 弟，

dà jiā lǒng lái zuò bǎ xì
大 家 拢 来 做 把 戏。

bǎ xì zuò de duō
把 戏 做 得 多，

dà jiā xiào hē hē
大 家 笑 呵 呵。

bǎ xì zuò de shǎo
把 戏 做 得 少，

dà jiā bú yào chǎo
大 家 不 要 吵。

zuò gè
做 个：

huáng lóng chū dòng
黄 龙 出 洞，

qiān niú guò hé
牵 牛 过 河，

zéi er tōu jī
贼 儿 偷 鸡，

huáng shǔ láng yǎo jī pó
黄 鼠 狼 咬 鸡 婆，

léi gōng dǎ zhū
雷 公 打 猪。

qiān qiān chě chě tuō tuō
牵 牵 扯 扯 拖 拖，

xī xī hā hā hē hē
嘻 嘻 哈 哈 呵 呵，

dà jiā pāi shǒu chàng gē
大 家 拍 手 唱 歌。

小雨滴
xiǎo yǔ dī

（中国台湾）麦穗

小雨滴从老远老远的地方跑来

跑到我家门前

有的敲敲厚厚的木瓜叶

有的去踩踩满池的睡莲

还有些在瓦片上跳舞

或躲在树林子里说悄悄话

他们像来自另一个星球

对这里的一切都感到新奇

tā men nà gǔ táo qì de wán pí jìn
他 们 那 股 淘 气 的 顽 皮 劲

shí zú xiàng yì qún xiǎo xiǎo de liú làng ér
十 足 像 一 群 小 小 的 流 浪 儿

多可爱的小雨滴呀！顽皮又淘气，充满了活力。诗人用拟人的手法，把小雨滴比拟成来自另一个星球的流浪儿，会蹦会跳，还会说悄悄话呢！你喜欢他们吗？

lù   zhū
露　珠

rì běn jīn zǐ měi líng
[日本]金子美铃

shéi dōu bú yào gào su
谁 都 不 要 告 诉

hǎo ma
好 吗？

qīng chén tíng yuàn de
清 晨 庭 院 的

jiǎo luò li
角 落 里，

huā er qiāo qiāo
花 儿 悄 悄

diào yǎn lèi de shì
掉 眼 泪 的 事。

wàn yī zhè shì
万 一 这 事

shuō chu qu le
说 出 去 了，

chuán dào
传 到

mì fēng de ěr duo li
蜜 蜂 的 耳 朵 里，

tā huì xiàng
它 会 像

zuò le kuī xīn shì yí yàng
做 了 亏 心 事 一 样，

fēi hui qu
飞 回 去

huán fēng mì ba
还 蜂 蜜 吧。

wú fēi   yì
（吴 菲　译）

赏析　　清晨，花儿上的露珠在诗人的眼里成了眼泪。有了情感，大自然的事情就有了更多的情趣和意味。所以，诗人由露珠想到蜜蜂回来还蜂蜜，多么可爱的想法啊！读来总让我们生出许多感动。

huǒ chē tóu
火 车 头

[波 兰] 图 维 姆

一排大轮子转起来，

越 转 越 快，

一节节车厢在我眼前闪过去，

它们都变得这样轻，

轻得呀就像是一个个的皮球！

切里咔嚓，

切里咔嚓，

切里咔嚓！

（韦苇 译）

山 中
shān zhōng

（唐）王 维
táng wáng wéi

荆 溪 白 石 出 ①，
jīng xī bái shí chū

天 寒 红 叶 稀。
tiān hán hóng yè xī

山 路 元 无 雨 ②，
shān lù yuán wú yǔ

空 翠 湿 人 衣。
kōng cuì shī rén yī

注释

① 荆溪：本名长水，发源于秦岭山中，流经长安县东北汇入灞水。

② 元：原来，本来。

第三单元

十二月子

◎ 民间童谣

正月十五汤圆子，
二月惊蛰喂丸子，
三月清明下种子，
四月芒种栽秧子，
五月端阳包粽子，
六月天热扇扇子，

七月中旬舂谷子，
八月十五杀鸭子，
九月重阳扬谷子，
十月小雪穿袄子，
冬月天寒杀蝗子，
腊月除夕吃饺子。

shù
树

◎ 张 秋 生

森林里被锯掉一棵树
熊就在他的画册上
画下一棵树
森林被锯掉两棵树
熊就在他的画册上
画下两棵树

……

熊时常翻开画册,对他已经
不再存在的朋友说:
要是你们还在
这世界该有多好

xī yáng
夕 阳

zhōng guó tái wān féng huī yuè
（中 国 台 湾）冯 辉 岳

hóng hóng de xī yáng
红 红 的 夕 阳，

zhào zài dàn shuǐ hé shang
照 在 淡 水 河 上。

xiǎo chuán na
小 船 哪!

nǐ qīng qīng de yáo dàng
你 轻 轻 地 摇 荡，

shì zài wǎng yú
是 在 网 鱼，

hái shì wǎng nà jīn huáng de bō làng
还 是 网 那 金 黄 的 波 浪?

赏析　　这首诗勾勒了一幅美丽的画面。用"红红"与"金黄"写出了夕阳落在水中的美景。本文用了一个问句，激起了读者无穷无尽的想象。

16

青蛙

qīng wā

◎ 凌 非

líng fēi

wǒ bēi zhe shū bāo shàng xué de shí hou xiǎng
我背着书包上学的时候想

qīng wā rú guǒ yě bēi zhe shū bāo
青蛙如果也背着书包

wǎng qián tiào
往前跳

nà yí dìng hěn hǎo wán
那一定很好玩

wǒ zuò zǎo cāo de shí hou xiǎng
我做早操的时候想

qīng wā rú guǒ yě pái zhe duì
青蛙如果也排着队

zuò zǎo cāo
做早操

nà yí dìng hěn hǎo wán
那一定很好玩

wǒ zǒu dào jiào shì li de shí hou xiǎng
我 走 到 教 室 里 的 时 候 想

zài hēi bǎn shang xiě zì de lǎo shī yì zhuǎn shēn
在 黑 板 上 写 字 的 老 师 一 转 身

fā xiàn yì zhī qīng wā zhèng gǔ zhe yǎn jing kàn zhe tā
发 现 一 只 青 蛙 正 鼓 着 眼 睛 看 着 她

nà yí dìng hěn hǎo wán
那 一 定 很 好 玩

rú guǒ lǎo shī zhī dào
如 果 老 师 知 道

qīng wā shì wǒ fàng zài jiǎng tái shang de huà
青 蛙 是 我 放 在 讲 台 上 的 话

nà yí dìng hěn bù hǎo wán
那 …… 一 定 很 不 好 玩

 赏析

孩子的想象,孩子的思维,前面三节是孩子和青蛙的比较,结构相似,意趣盎然。最后一节"那……一定很不好玩"让人忍俊不禁,活脱脱勾勒出一个淘气的孩子形象。

shān zhōng
山 中

táng wáng bó
（唐）王 勃

cháng jiāng bēi yǐ zhì
长 江 悲 已 滞 ①，

wàn lǐ niàn jiāng guī
万 里 念 将 归 ②。

kuàng shǔ gāo fēng wǎn
况 属 高 风 晚 ③，

shān shān huáng yè fēi
山 山 黄 叶 飞 。

① 滞：淹留，停住。
② 念将归：想要回家。
③ 高风：山中吹来的风。

第四单元

xiǎo yuē kǎ xué gàn zhēn xiàn huó
小约卡学干针线活

jié kè sī luò fá kè   běn duō wá
[捷克斯洛伐克] 本多娃

xiǎo yuē kǎ zhǎo dào le zhēn hé xiàn
小约卡找到了针和线，

tā féng le xiē shén me   nǐ mǎ shàng huì qiáo jiàn
她缝了些什么？你马上会瞧见。

xiān shi bà ba shēng qì yòu chī jīng
先是爸爸生气又吃惊：

wǒ de shàng yī zěn me chuān bú jìn
"我的上衣怎么穿不进?!"

jiē zhe mā ma fān lái fù qù de qiáo
接着妈妈翻来覆去地瞧：

wǒ de mào zi zěn me dài bù liǎo
"我的帽子怎么戴不了?"

yé ye rǎng zhe　　bú xiàng huà
爷爷嚷着:"不 像 话!

shéi bǎ wǒ hé tǎng yǐ féng zài yì qǐ la
谁 把 我 和 躺 椅 缝 在 一 起 啦!"

gū gu chuān bú jìn qún
姑 姑 穿 不 进 裙,

shū shu chuān bú jìn kù hé wà
叔 叔 穿 不 进 裤 和 袜。

xiǎo yuē kǎ xiào de lè kāi le huā
小 约 卡 笑 得 乐 开 了 花,

qiáo zán jiā lián yí gè kū long yě méi yǒu la
"瞧,咱 家 连 一 个 窟 窿 也 没 有 啦!"

liú xīng càn　　yì
(刘 星 灿 译)

赏析　　这首诗并没有直接写小约卡是如何干针线活的,但是从家人的反应中,我们自然会看出这活儿究竟干得怎样。这首诗视角独特,把一个喜欢尝试的可爱的小女孩形象栩栩如生地展现在我们面前。

安 慰

◎ 顾 城

青青的野葡萄

淡黄的小月亮

妈妈发愁了

怎么做果酱

我说：

别加糖

在早晨的篱笆上

有一枚甜甜的

红太阳

海上的风

◎ 刘饶民

海上的风是花神,
她一来,
就绽开万朵浪花……

海上的风是大力士,
他一来,
就送走万片渔帆……

海上的风是琴师,
她一来,
就奏出万种歌声……

海上的风是狮子,
它一吼,
就掀起波浪滔天……

赏析

　　海上的风千姿百态,在诗人眼里成了花神、琴师、大力士……这些奇妙的想象展现了大海的万般风情,令人神往。在你眼里,海上的风又是什么?

23

妈妈的心

（中国台湾）林焕彰

妈妈的心，
像我的影子
总是跟着我走的。

早晨，我去上学
在教室里念书的时候
她就躲在我的耳朵里，
悄悄地说：
要认真读书哦。

我在外面游戏的时候
她就跑出来，
有时，在我面前
有时，在我背后
有时，在我左右
总是悄悄地说：
小心，小心，
不要跌倒哦！

zá shī
杂 诗

táng wáng wéi
（唐）王 维

jūn zì gù xiāng lái
君 自 故 乡 来，

yīng zhī gù xiāng shì
应 知 故 乡 事。

lái rì qǐ chuāng qián
来 日 绮 窗 前 ①，

hán méi zhuó huā wèi
寒 梅 著 花 未 ②？

① 来日：来的时候。绮窗：雕镂花纹的窗子。
② 著花：开花。

25

第五单元

zhù zi hé shù zi
柱子和树子

◎ 民间童谣

有个小孩子叫柱子，
割草丢了灰兔子；
有个小孩子叫树子，
玩水丢了花裤子；
柱子去找灰兔子，
捡到一条花裤子；
树子去找花裤子，
拾到一只灰兔子；
树子把兔子还给柱子，
柱子把裤子还给树子。

26

老祖母的牙齿
lǎo zǔ mǔ de yá chǐ

（中国台湾）曾妙容
zhōng guó tái wān zēng miào róng

时间真是恶作剧，
shí jiān zhēn shì è zuò jù

爱在老祖母的牙齿上开山洞；
ài zài lǎo zǔ mǔ de yá chǐ shang kāi shān dòng

风儿更顽皮，
fēng er gèng wán pí

在那山洞里钻来钻去。
zài nà shān dòng li zuān lái zuān qù

嘘！嘘！嘘！
xū xū xū

老祖母的话儿半天才说一句：
lǎo zǔ mǔ de huà er bàn tiān cái shuō yí jù

去！去！去！
qù qù qù

逗得我们笑嘻嘻。
dòu de wǒ men xiào xī xī

赏析

　　用"时间爱在老祖母的牙齿上开山洞"来表现"祖母的牙齿掉光了"，这个巧妙的比喻，听起来格外有情趣！"嘘"和"去"这两个形容牙齿漏风的词语，叠起来一念，就更加活泼有趣了。反复读几遍，你会感受到声音的快乐。

zháo jí de guō zi
着 急 的 锅 子

（中 国 台 湾）谢 武 彰

吃 午 饭 的 时 候 到 了
菜 却 还 没 煮 好
弟 弟 等 得 好 急 了
妹 妹 等 得 好 急 了
小 猫 等 得 好 急 了
只 有 妈 妈 最 辛 苦 了

还 不 停 地 忙 着
急 得 脸 上 都 是 汗
我 赶 快 来 帮 忙
打 开 锅 子 一 看
呀！锅 子 也 急 坏 了
它 也 满 头 大 汗 呢！

赏析　　短短的几行诗，刻画了开饭前家中忙碌的情景。最妙的是最后一句，把锅盖上点点滴滴的水珠，写成了着急时的"满头大汗"，比喻奇妙，让我们感受到家的温暖。

作业机

[美国]谢尔·希尔弗斯坦

作业机,哦,作业机,

世界上最完美的机器。

只要把作业放进去,再投进一角硬币,

按下按钮,等上十秒,

你的作业就会出来,

又干净,又整齐。

来看看——"9+4=?"答案是"3"。

3?

哦,我的天!

看来它没有我想的那么神奇。

(叶硕 译)

qiū yè jì qiū yuán wài
秋 夜 寄 邱 员 外 ①

táng wéi yìng wù
（唐）韦 应 物

huái jūn shǔ qiū yè
怀 君 属 秋 夜 ②，

sàn bù yǒng liáng tiān
散 步 咏 凉 天 。

kōng shān sōng zǐ luò
空 山 松 子 落 ，

yōu rén yīng wèi mián
幽 人 应 未 眠 ③ 。

① 邱员外：名丹，苏州人，曾做官，后隐居临平山学道。
② 属：适逢，正值，正当。
③ 幽人：悠闲的人，这里指邱员外。

cuò le gē
错 了 歌

◎ mín jiān tóng yáo
◎ 民 间 童 谣

gāng guò shí èr diǎn tài yáng jiù luò pō
刚 过 十 二 点，太 阳 就 落 坡。

yā zi táo shàng shù māo er jìn le wō
鸭 子 逃 上 树，猫 儿 进 了 窝。

biān fú tiān shang fēi zhèng bǎ mì fēng zhuō
蝙 蝠 天 上 飞，正 把 蜜 蜂 捉。

gǒu er bú pà rè shé tou zuǐ biān tuō
狗 儿 不 怕 热，舌 头 嘴 边 拖。

fēi lái yíng huǒ chóng bǎ wǒ shǒu tàng pò
飞 来 萤 火 虫，把 我 手 烫 破。

wén zi wēng wēng jiào zhí wǎng dēng shang luò
蚊 子 嗡 嗡 叫，直 往 灯 上 落。

yuè yuán xīng xing duō zěn néng bú chàng gē
月 圆 星 星 多，怎 能 不 唱 歌？

qǐng nǐ xiǎng yì xiǎng chàng cuò méi chàng cuò
请 你 想 一 想，唱 错 没 唱 错？

wǒ yào shēng qǐ qì lai
我 要 生 起 气 来

jié kè sī luò fá kè nài zī wǎ ěr
[捷克斯洛伐克]奈兹瓦尔

wǒ yào shēng qǐ qì lai
我 要 生 起 气 来，

jiù yí gè rén dào fēi zhōu qù
就 一 个 人 到 非 洲 去。

wǒ yǒu yí jù mù mǎ
我 有 一 具 木 马，

wǒ qí zhe tā yuǎn yuǎn de pǎo diào
我 骑 着 它 远 远 地 跑 掉。

zài fēi zhōu è le wǒ chī chéng zi
在 非 洲，饿 了 我 吃 橙 子。

mā ma bà ba nǎi nai lǎo lao
妈 妈，爸 爸，奶 奶，姥 姥，

wǒ yí gè yě bù xiǎng niàn
我 一 个 也 不 想 念，

yào shi wǒ xīn li bù hǎo shòu
要 是 我 心 里 不 好 受，

wǒ yě bú huì kū bú huì shāng xīn
我 也 不 会 哭，不 会 伤 心。

fēi zhōu yǒu xǔ duō hú dié
非　洲　有　许　多　蝴　蝶，

tā men yì tiān gāo gāo xìng xìng de
它　们　一　天　高　高　兴　兴　的，

tā men huì fēi dào wǒ tóu shang lai
它　们　会　飞　到　我　头　上　来，

gěi wǒ jiǎng gè zhǒng gè yàng de gù shi
给　我　讲　各　种　各　样　的　故　事，

nà shēng yīn xiàng mèng qīng qīng de
那　声　音　像　梦，轻　轻　的。

wéi wéi yì
（韦　苇　译）

wǒ gěi xiǎo jī qǐ míng zi
我 给 小 鸡 起 名 字

rén róng róng
◎ 任 溶 溶

yī èr sān sì wǔ liù qī
一、二、三、四、五、六、七，

mā ma mǎi le qī zhī jī
妈 妈 买 了 七 只 鸡。

wǒ gěi xiǎo jī qǐ míng zi
我 给 小 鸡 起 名 字：

xiǎo yī
小 一

xiǎo èr
小 二

xiǎo sān
小 三

xiǎo sì
小 四

xiǎo wǔ
小 五

xiǎo liù
小 六

xiǎo qī
小 七。

tā men yí xià dōu zǒu sàn
它 们 一 下 都 走 散，

yì zhī dōng lái yì zhī xī
一 只 东 来 一 只 西。

yú shì zài yě rèn bù chū
于 是 再 也 认 不 出，

shéi shì xiǎo qī
谁 是 小 七，

xiǎo liù
小 六，

xiǎo wǔ
小 五，

xiǎo sì
小 四，

xiǎo sān
小 三，

xiǎo èr
小 二，

xiǎo yī
小 一。

赏析

这是首非常巧妙的数字诗。数字巧妙地贯穿在童趣盎然的
故事情节里，让整首诗充满了节奏感，也让我们看到了一个可爱
的孩子形象。

<ruby>日<rt>rì</rt></ruby> <ruby>出<rt>chū</rt></ruby>

<ruby>（中国台湾）<rt>zhōng guó tái wān</rt></ruby> <ruby>林焕彰<rt>lín huàn zhāng</rt></ruby>

<ruby>早晨，<rt>zǎo chen</rt></ruby>

<ruby>太阳是一个娃娃，<rt>tài yáng shì yí gè wá wa</rt></ruby>

<ruby>一睡醒就不停地<rt>yí shuì xǐng jiù bù tíng de</rt></ruby>

<ruby>踢着蓝被子，<rt>tī zhe lán bèi zi</rt></ruby>

<ruby>很久很久，才慢慢慢慢地<rt>hěn jiǔ hěn jiǔ cái màn màn màn màn de</rt></ruby>

<ruby>露出一个<rt>lù chū yí gè</rt></ruby>

<ruby>圆圆胖胖的<rt>yuán yuán pàng pàng de</rt></ruby>

<ruby>脸儿。<rt>liǎn er</rt></ruby>

赏析

娃娃起床时，总是淘气地踢着被子，然后才慢慢地爬起来。太阳呢？每天起床是不是总和娃娃一个样？形象的比喻让"日出"多了许多的情趣！在你眼里，太阳是不是更加可爱了？

九日
jiǔ   rì

táng wáng bó
（唐）王 勃

jiǔ rì chóng yáng jié
九 日 重 阳 节，

kāi mén yǒu jú huā
开 门 有 菊 花。

bù zhī lái sòng jiǔ
不 知 来 送 酒，

ruò gè shì táo jiā
若 个 是 陶 家 ①。

① 若个：哪个。陶家：陶渊明的家。

第七单元

hǔ hé tù
虎 和 兔

wú chéng
◎ 吴 珹

pō shang yǒu zhī dà lǎo hǔ
坡 上 有 只 大 老 虎，

pō xià yǒu zhī xiǎo huī tù
坡 下 有 只 小 灰 兔；

lǎo hǔ è dù du
老 虎 饿 肚 肚，

xiǎng chī huī tù tu
想 吃 灰 兔 兔。

hǔ zhuī tù tù duǒ hǔ
虎 追 兔，兔 躲 虎，

lǎo hǔ mǎn pō zhǎo huī tù
老 虎 满 坡 找 灰 兔；

tù zuān wō hǔ pū tù
兔 钻 窝，虎 扑 兔，

cì er zhā tòng hǔ pì gu
刺 儿 扎 痛 虎 屁 股。

qì huài le hǔ
气 坏 了 虎，

lè huài le tù
乐 坏 了 兔；

è hǔ dù li gū gū gū
饿 虎 肚 里 咕 咕 咕，

xiào huài wō li huī tù tu
笑 坏 窝 里 灰 兔 兔。

赏析　老虎和兔子，一只强来一只弱。善良的人们，可不希望兔子被吃掉，于是，兔子安全了，老虎吃亏了。反复读这首谐趣的动物儿歌，可以感受到弱者胜利的快乐。"虎"和"兔"一不小心，就会读错，可要细心点哟！

小 熊

[苏联]托克玛科娃

下雪啰，

整个山上雪呀雪，

下雪啰，

整个山下雪呀雪，

下雪啰，

枞树上面雪呀雪。

雪下小熊睡得香，

轻点，轻点，

安静，安静，

小熊做梦甜又甜，

轻点，轻点，

安静，安静……

（韦苇 译）

吊床
diào chuáng

měi guó xiè ěr xī ěr fú sī tǎn
[美国]谢尔·希尔弗斯坦

nǎi nai sòng lái le diào chuáng
奶奶送来了吊床，

lǎo tiān gōng gong sòng lái le qīng fēng yáng
老天公公送来了清风扬。

wǒ xiǎng shū shū fu fu tǎng shàng diào chuáng
我想舒舒服服躺上吊床——

xiàn zài shéi qù bǎ shù nuó guo lai
现在，谁去把树挪过来？

yè shuò yì
（叶硕 译）

zǎo ān xiǎo sōng shǔ
早 安，小 松 鼠

xīn jiā pō liú kě shì
[新加坡] 刘可式

zǎo ān xiǎo sōng shǔ
早 安，小 松 鼠

zhěng gè zǎo chen
整 个 早 晨

wǒ yì zhí kàn zhe nǐ
我 一 直 看 着 你

zěn yàng bǎ měi yí cùn
怎 样 把 每 一 寸

líng lóng de chén guāng
玲 珑 的 晨 光

biàn zuò qī cǎi de tiào yuè
变 作 七 彩 的 跳 跃

jiáo chéng sōng zǐ de guǒ xiāng
嚼 成 松 子 的 果 香

赏析　　你看到了吗？晨光中，松鼠在跳跃，在吃松子……有了这样一只可爱的小精灵领着，奇妙而充满活力的一天又开始了！

遗爱寺 ①
yí ài sì

（唐）白居易
táng bái jū yì

弄 石 临 溪 坐②，
nòng shí lín xī zuò

寻 花 绕 寺 行。
xún huā rào sì xíng

时 时 闻 鸟 语，
shí shí wén niǎo yǔ

处 处 是 泉 声。
chù chù shì quán shēng

注释

① 遗爱寺：在今庐山香炉峰下。
② 弄：玩。

第八单元

diū shǒu pà gē
丢 手 帕 歌

◎ mín jiān tóng yáo
◎ 民 间 童 谣

hú lu gēn
葫 芦 根，

hú lu wàn
葫 芦 蔓，

bù zhī xiǎo hú lu
不 知 小 葫 芦

zhòng nǎ kuài
种 哪 块？

zhòng tiān shàng
种 天 上？

pà huǒ shāo
怕 火 烧。

zhòng dì shang
种 地 上？

pà shuǐ lào
怕 水 涝。

zhòng yuàn li
种 院 里？

pà rén tōu
怕 人 偷。

zhòng wū li
种 屋 里？

hài pà diū
害 怕 丢。

gāng xiǎng yào zhòng lì le qiū
刚 想 要 种 立 了 秋。

游戏
yóu xì

（中国台湾）詹冰
zhōng guó tái wān zhān bīng

"小弟弟，我们来游戏。
xiǎo dì di wǒ men lái yóu xì

姐姐当老师，
jiě jie dāng lǎo shī

你当学生。"
nǐ dāng xué sheng

"姐姐，那么，小妹妹呢？"
jiě jie nà me xiǎo mèi mei ne

"小妹妹太小了，
xiǎo mèi mei tài xiǎo le

她什么也不会做。
tā shén me yě bú huì zuò

我看——
wǒ kàn

让她当校长算了。"
ràng tā dāng xiào zhǎng suàn le

赏析　这首对话式的童诗用的是孩子的语言，表达了孩子的想法，读起来会引起快活的笑声。可仔细一想，姐姐的话是不是也有些道理呢？

挤 呀 挤

◎ 郑 春 华

挤 呀 挤

黑 夜 想 挤 开 树

树 牢 牢 的

挤 呀 挤

黑 夜 想 挤 倒 屋

屋 稳 稳 的

挤 呀 挤

黑 夜 因 为 太 用 力

把 太 阳 挤 出 了 大 地

草　原

cǎo　　yuán

rì běn jīn zǐ měi líng
[日本]金子美铃

露水晶莹的草原
lù shui jīng yíng de cǎo yuán

如果光着脚走过，
rú guǒ guāng zhe jiǎo zǒu guo

脚一定会染得绿绿的吧。
jiǎo yí dìng huì rǎn de lǜ lǜ de ba

一定会沾上青草的味道吧。
yí dìng huì zhān shàng qīng cǎo de wèi dao ba

如果这样走啊走
rú guǒ zhè yàng zǒu a zǒu

直到变成一棵草，
zhí dào biàn chéng yì kē cǎo

我的脸蛋儿，会变成
wǒ de liǎn dàn er huì biàn chéng

一朵美丽的花儿，开放吧。
yì duǒ měi lì de huā er kāi fàng ba

wú fēi yì
（吴菲　译）

赏析

绿绿的、大大的草原，总会引发无限的想象。让我们跟着诗人走呀走，直到心中也开出美丽的花儿吧！

46

塞下曲六首（其二）

sài xià qǔ liù shǒu qí èr

táng lú lún
（唐）卢纶

lín àn cǎo jīng fēng
林 暗 草 惊 风，

jiāng jūn yè yǐn gōng
将 军 夜 引 弓①。

píng míng xún bái yǔ
平 明 寻 白 羽②，

mò zài shí léng zhōng
没 在 石 棱 中③。

注释

① 引：拉开弓。
② 平明：清早。白羽：古代箭名，箭杆上饰有白色羽毛。
③ 没：陷入。

第九单元

sūn wù kōng dǎ yāo guài
孙 悟 空 打 妖 怪

fán jiā xìn
◎ 樊 家 信

táng sēng qí mǎ dōng nà ge dōng
唐 僧 骑 马 咚 那 个 咚，

hòu miàn gēn zhe gè sūn wù kōng
后 面 跟 着 个 孙 悟 空。

sūn wù kōng pǎo de kuài
孙 悟 空，跑 得 快，

hòu miàn gēn zhe gè zhū bā jiè
后 面 跟 着 个 猪 八 戒。

zhū bā jiè bí zi cháng
猪 八 戒，鼻 子 长，

hòu miàn gēn zhe gè shā hé shang
后 面 跟 着 个 沙 和 尚。

shā hé shang tiāo zhe luó
沙 和 尚，挑 着 箩，

hòu miàn lái le lǎo yāo pó
后 面 来 了 老 妖 婆。

lǎo yāo pó zhēn jiào huài
老 妖 婆，真 叫 坏，

piàn guò táng sēng hé bā jiè
骗 过 唐 僧 和 八 戒。

táng sēng bā jiè zhēn hú tu
唐 僧 八 戒 真 糊 涂，

shì rén shì yāo fēn bù chū
是 人 是 妖 分 不 出。

fēn bù chū shàng le dàng
分 不 出，上 了 当，

duō kuī sūn wù kōng yǎn jing liàng
多 亏 孙 悟 空 眼 睛 亮。

yǎn jing liàng mào jīn guāng
眼 睛 亮，冒 金 光，

gāo gāo jǔ qǐ jīn gū bàng
高 高 举 起 金 箍 棒。

jīn gū bàng yǒu lì liàng
金 箍 棒，有 力 量，

yāo mó guǐ guài xiāo miè guāng
妖 魔 鬼 怪 消 灭 光。

wō niú
蜗 牛

（中国台湾）林良

不要再说我慢

这种话

我已经听过几万遍

我最后再说一次

这是为了交通安全

赏析　　说起蜗牛，大家都会认为它慢。可诗人却不这样认为，蜗牛的慢是为了交通安全！这是一个很特别的想法，仔细回味，还真有趣！

湖 边 的 小 草

（中 国 台 湾）林 芳 萍

湖 边 的 小 草 说

树 比 我 高　山 比 树 高

云 比 山 高　天 空 比 云 高

但 是 当 我 弯 下 腰

天 空 掉 进 湖 水 里

我 比 天 空 还 要 高

赏析　当我们换一个角度看问题，就会有不一样的结果，就像"我"弯下腰看湖水里的天空。这首小诗想象大胆，构思独特，读来让人轻松、愉快而又有思考。

笼中虎
（lóng zhōng hǔ）

[俄罗斯]拉什科夫斯基
（é luó sī lā shí kē fū sī jī）

一只小老鼠来到动物园。
（yì zhī xiǎo lǎo shǔ lái dào dòng wù yuán）

看见老虎就咧嘴笑了：
（kàn jiàn lǎo hǔ jiù liě zuǐ xiào le）

"嗨，你这猫，到底
（hēi nǐ zhè māo dào dǐ）

也让鼠笼给逮住了！"
（yě ràng shǔ lóng gěi dǎi zhù le）

（韦苇 译）
（wéi wéi yì）

马　诗（其四）
mǎ　shī（qí sì）

（唐）李贺
táng lǐ hè

此 马 非 凡 马，
cǐ mǎ fēi fán mǎ

房 星 本 是 星①。
fáng xīng běn shì xīng

向 前 敲 瘦 骨②，
xiàng qián qiāo shòu gǔ

犹 自 带 铜 声③。
yóu zì dài tóng shēng

① 房星：星宿名，属二十八宿的东方七宿，也称天驷、天马。
② 瘦骨：据说良马大多瘦骏。
③ "犹自"句：形容良马骏骨坚劲，犹如铁打铜铸。

第十单元

bǎn dèng wāi wāi
板 凳 歪 歪

mín jiān tóng yáo
◎ 民 间 童 谣

bǎn dèng bǎn dèng wāi wāi
板凳板凳歪歪，

lǐ miàn zuò gè guāi guāi
里面坐个乖乖；

guāi guāi chū lai mǎi cài
乖乖出来买菜，

lǐ miàn zuò gè nǎi nai
里面坐个奶奶；

nǎi nai chū lai shāo tāng
奶奶出来烧汤，

lǐ miàn zuò gè gū niang
里面坐个姑娘；

gū niang chū lai shū tóu
姑娘出来梳头，

lǐ miàn zuò gè xiǎo hóu
里面坐个小猴；

xiǎo hóu chū lai zuò yī
小猴出来作揖，

lǐ mian zuò gè gōng jī
里面坐个公鸡；

gōng jī chū lai dǎ míng
公鸡出来打鸣，

lǐ mian zuò gè dòu chóng
里面坐个豆虫；

dòu chóng chū lai pá pa
豆虫出来爬爬，

lǐ mian zuò zhe há ma
里面坐着蛤蟆；

há ma yí dèng yǎn
蛤蟆一瞪眼，

qī gè dié zi bā gè wǎn
七个碟子八个碗。

53

小 树

[苏联]拉·法尔哈季

"小树，

你在我们园子都做些什么？"

"春天的早晨

我往高处长，

长得高高！"

"那么晚上

你在我们园子都做些什么？"

"晚上，

wǒ de yè zi dōu chéng le xiǎo shǒu
我 的 叶 子 都 成 了 小 手，

zhǎng xīn bǎ xīng xing gāo gāo tuō zhe
掌 心 把 星 星 高 高 托 着！"

赏析

"小树，你在我们园子都做些什么？"小诗以充满童趣的问答展开。早晨，小树往高处长，充满活力；晚上，小树的叶子变成了小手，把星星高高托着。小树的形象更加丰满、生动了。

树　林

shù　　　lín

（中国台湾）谢明芳
zhōng guó tái wān　xiè míng fāng

一棵、两棵、三棵……
yì　kē　liǎng kē　sān　kē

好多棵树，
hǎo duō kē shù

有的在玩一二三木头人，
yǒu de zài wán yī èr sān mù tou rén

有的模仿电线杆，
yǒu de mó fǎng diàn xiàn gān

有的被妈妈罚站，
yǒu de bèi mā ma fá zhàn

有的摆好姿势在照相，
yǒu de bǎi hǎo zī shì zài zhào xiàng

不动，不动，
bú dòng bú dòng

大家专心地——不动！
dà jiā zhuān xīn de bú dòng

赏析　　兔子可以奔跑，风可以跳跃，树呢？大家都不动。仔细地观察，每棵树都有自己的样子，都在做着自己喜欢的事情。小朋友，你眼中的树又在忙什么呢？

qiū tiān de xìn
秋 天 的 信

zhōng guó tái wān　lín wǔ xiàn
（中 国 台 湾）林 武 宪

qiū tiān yào gěi dà jiā xiě xìn
秋 天 要 给 大 家 写 信

yòng yè zi zuò xìn zhǐ
用 叶 子 做 信 纸

qǐng fēng dāng yóu chāi
请 风 当 邮 差

tōu lǎn de yóu chāi
偷 懒 的 邮 差

měi dào yí gè dì fang
每 到 一 个 地 方

jiù bǎ xìn yì pāo
就 把 信 一 抛

yǒu de xìn luò zài sōng shǔ tóu shang
有 的 信, 落 在 松 鼠 头 上

yǒu de xìn diào zài qīng wā shēn páng
有 的 信, 掉 在 青 蛙 身 旁

gǎn lù de yàn yě xián le yí yè huí jiā
赶 路 的 雁, 也 衔 了 一 页 回 家

chí táng li cǎo cóng zhōng
池 塘 里, 草 丛 中

dào chù dōu yǒu qiū tiān de xìn
到 处 都 有 秋 天 的 信

dòng wù men jí máng zhǔn bèi guò dōng
动 物 们 急 忙 准 备 过 冬

自 遣 ①
zì qiǎn

（唐）李 白
táng lǐ bái

对 酒 不 觉 暝 ②，
duì jiǔ bù jué míng

落 花 盈 我 衣 ③。
luò huā yíng wǒ yī

醉 起 步 溪 月，
zuì qǐ bù xī yuè

鸟 还 人 亦 稀。
niǎo huán rén yì xī

注释

① 自遣：自己排遣愁闷，宽慰自己。

② 对酒：与人对饮。暝：日暮。

③ 盈：满。

xiǎo dì hé xiǎo māo
小 弟 和 小 猫

◎ 柯岩

wǒ jiā yǒu gè xiǎo dì di
我 家 有 个 小 弟 弟，

cōng míng yòu táo qì
聪 明 又 淘 气，

měi tiān pá gāo yòu pá dī
每 天 爬 高 又 爬 低，

mǎn tóu mǎn liǎn dōu shì ní
满 头 满 脸 都 是 泥。

mā ma jiào tā lái xǐ zǎo
妈 妈 叫 他 来 洗 澡，

zhuāng méi tīng jiàn tā jiù pǎo
装 没 听 见 他 就 跑，

bà ba ná jìng zi bǎ tā zhào
爸 爸 拿 镜 子 把 他 照，

tā bì shàng yǎn jing gē gē de xiào
他 闭 上 眼 睛 咯 咯 地 笑。

jiě jie bào lái gè xiǎo huā māo
姐姐抱来个小花猫，

pāi pai zhuǎ zi tiǎn tian máo
拍拍爪子舔舔毛，

liǎng yǎn yì mī miào miào miào
两眼一眯"妙，妙，妙，

shéi gēn wǒ wán shéi bǎ wǒ bào
谁跟我玩，谁把我抱？"

dì di shēn chū xiǎo hēi shǒu
弟弟伸出小黑手，

xiǎo māo lián máng wǎng hòu tiào
小猫连忙往后跳，

hú zi yì juē tóu yì yáo
胡子一撅头一摇：

bú miào bú miào
"不妙不妙！

tài zāng tài zāng wǒ bú yào
太脏太脏我不要！"

jiě jie tīng jiàn hā hā xiào
姐姐听见哈哈笑，

bà ba mā ma zhòu méi mao
爸爸妈妈皱眉毛，

xiǎo dì tīng le zhēn hài sào
小弟听了真害臊：

mā mā kuài kuài gěi wǒ xǐ gè zǎo
"妈！妈！快快给我洗个澡！"

biāo diǎn fú hào
标 点 符 号

◎ 丁 云

mā ma shì dòu hào
妈 妈 是 逗 号，
zhěng tiān láo láo dāo dāo
整 天 唠 唠 叨 叨
méi wán méi liǎo
没 完 没 了。

bà ba shì mào hào
爸 爸 是 冒 号，
fā hào shī lìng wēi fēng de
发 号 施 令 威 风 得
bù dé liǎo
不 得 了。

wǒ shì shěng lüè hào
我 是 省 略 号，
shuō huà yǒu diǎn jiē ba
说 话 有 点 结 巴
zǒng shì rě rén xiào
总 是 惹 人 笑。

nà yé ye ne
那 爷 爷 呢？
āi hái tǎng zài yī yuàn li
唉！还 躺 在 医 院 里，
nà tā zhǐ hǎo dāng bìng hào
那 他 只 好 当 病 号。

赏析　　用标点符号来代表家庭成员，多形象的表达呀！最妙的是各种标点符号都给家庭成员准确地定位。出人意料的结尾，让人眼睛一亮，又让人感受到了满满的童心。

nián líng wèn tí
年 龄 问 题

zhōng guó tái wān dù róng chēn
（ 中 国 台 湾 ）杜 荣 琛

yé ye de nián líng
爷 爷 的 年 龄，

xiě zài liǎn shang de zhòu wén li
写 在 脸 上 的 皱 纹 里；

mǎ er de nián líng
马 儿 的 年 龄，

jiáo zài zuǐ ba de yá chǐ li
嚼 在 嘴 巴 的 牙 齿 里；

shù mù de nián líng
树 木 的 年 龄，

cáng zài dù zi de nián lún li
藏 在 肚 子 的 年 轮 里。

lǎo shī
老 师！

nà me chí táng de nián líng
那 么 池 塘 的 年 龄，

shì bú shì huà zài yì quān quān de lián yī li
是 不 是 画 在 一 圈 圈 的 涟 漪 里？

赏析

　　爷爷的年龄、马儿的年龄，我们都有办法知道。那池塘的年龄呢？看到了一圈圈的涟漪，让我们想到大树的年轮，那是不是池塘的年龄呢？认知的迁移，孩子的童言趣语，构成了一首可爱的童诗。

yí gè rén
一 个 人

qián wàn chéng
◎ 钱 万 成

yí gè rén
一 个 人

jiù xiàng yì kē xiǎo shù
就 像 一 棵 小 树

zhǐ yào lí kāi lín zi
只 要 离 开 林 子

jiù huì biàn de gū dú
就 会 变 得 孤 独

yí gè rén
一 个 人

jiù xiàng yì zhī xiǎo niǎo
就 像 一 只 小 鸟

zhǐ yǒu còu dào yì qǐ
只 有 凑 到 一 起

cái huì rè rè nào nào
才 会 热 热 闹 闹

yí gè rén
一 个 人

jiù xiàng yì tiáo xiǎo hé
就 像 一 条 小 河

zhǐ yǒu huì jù zài dà hǎi li
只 有 汇 聚 在 大 海 里

cái huì yōng yǒu kuài lè
才 会 拥 有 快 乐

yí gè rén
一 个 人

jiù xiàng yì kē xiǎo cǎo
就 像 一 棵 小 草

zhǐ yǒu dà jiā zhàn zài yì qǐ
只 有 大 家 站 在 一 起

cái bú huì bèi kuáng fēng chuī dǎo
才 不 会 被 狂 风 吹 倒

tīng tán qín
听 弹 琴

táng liú cháng qīng
（唐）刘 长 卿

líng líng qī xián shàng
冷 冷 七 弦 上①，

jìng tīng sōng fēng hán
静 听 松 风 寒②。

gǔ diào suī zì ài
古 调 虽 自 爱，

jīn rén duō bù tán
今 人 多 不 弹③。

注释

　　① 泠泠：本指水声，这里用以形容琴声的清越。七弦：古琴有七条弦，故称七弦琴。

　　② 松风寒：以寒风入松林比喻声音凄清，也指琴曲《风入松》。

　　③ 末两句：这《风入松》的古调，虽然我深深喜爱，但现在的人大多不弹了。

第十二单元

雪地给我拍照啦
xuě dì gěi wǒ pāi zhào la

◎ 胡木仁
hú mù rén

下雪啦，
xià xuě la

下雪啦
xià xuě la

遍地都是白花花。
biàn dì dōu shì bái huā huā

小妹妹，
xiǎo mèi mei

爱雪花，
ài xuě huā

清早起床
qīng zǎo qǐ chuáng

笑哈哈。
xiào hā hā

跑出门，
pǎo chū mén

摔倒啦，
shuāi dǎo la

雪地印个胖娃娃。
xuě dì yìn gè pàng wá wa

小妹妹，
xiǎo mèi mei

乐坏啦，
lè huài la

拍着小手叫妈妈：
pāi zhe xiǎo shǒu jiào mā ma

"快看啦，
kuài kàn la

快看啦，
kuài kàn la

雪地给我拍照啦！"
xuě dì gěi wǒ pāi zhào la

zài jiàn
再　见

◎ zhāng qiū shēng
张 秋 生

chūn tiān
春天，

bǎ mǎn shù de nèn yè zi
把满树的嫩叶子

jiāo gěi le xià jiě jie
交给了夏姐姐

tā shuō zài jiàn
——她说：再见。

xià tiān
夏天，

bǎ mǎn shù de qīng guǒ zi
把满树的青果子

jiāo gěi le qiū gū gu
交给了秋姑姑

tā shuō zài jiàn
——她说：再见。

qiū tiān
秋天，

bǎ shōu huò guo de guǒ yuán
把收获过的果园

jiāo gěi le dōng yé ye
交给了冬爷爷

tā shuō zài jiàn
——他说：再见。

dōng tiān
冬天，

yòng bái xuě dòng sǐ hài chóng
用白雪冻死害虫

bǎ kuài fā yá de guǒ yuán
把快发芽的果园

jiāo gěi chūn gū niang
交给春姑娘

tā shuō zài jiàn
——她说：再见！

shuǐ chí
水 池

[韩国] 赵 炳理

hǎo xiàng yě yǒu nián líng
好 像 也 有 年 龄

miàn duì zhe tā
面 对 着 它

tā mò mò bù jiǎng huà
它 默 默 不 讲 话

dàn tóu zhì shí tou
但 投 掷 石 头

tā jiù huí dá
它 就 回 答

yuán de yuán yuán de
圆 的 圆 圆 的

huá zhe yuán quān
划 着 圆 圈

bǎ zì jǐ de nián líng
把 自 己 的 年 龄

gào su wǒ men
告 诉 我 们

赏析　　水池默默的,不开口,可是等你投石问话,它也会回答。你看那一个个的圆圈,就是它的回答。多有趣的答案呀!

68

huān yíng xiǎo yǔ diǎn
欢 迎 小 雨 点

◎ 圣 野
shèng yě

来一点，
lái yì diǎn

不要太多。
bú yào tài duō

来一点，
lái yì diǎn

不要太少。
bú yào tài shǎo

来一点，
lái yì diǎn

泥土咧开了嘴巴等。
ní tǔ liě kāi le zuǐ ba děng

来一点，
lái yì diǎn

小菌们撑着小伞等。
xiǎo jūn men chēng zhe xiǎo sǎn děng

来一点，
lái yì diǎn

小荷叶站出水面来等。
xiǎo hé yè zhàn chū shuǐ miàn lái děng

小水塘笑了，
xiǎo shuǐ táng xiào le

一点一个笑窝。
yì diǎn yí gè xiào wō

小野菊笑了，
xiǎo yě jú xiào le

一点敬一个礼。
yì diǎn jìng yí gè lǐ

赏析　　小雨点要来了，大家都在热情地等待。小雨点来了，大家都在开心地微笑。快乐的节奏，活泼的语言，让这首诗充满意趣。一起来欢迎这不多也不少的小雨点吧！

忆　梅
yì　méi

（唐）李　商　隐

定　定　住　天　涯^①，
dìng　dìng　zhù　tiān　yá

依　依　向　物　华^②。
yī　yī　xiàng　wù　huá

寒　梅　最　堪　恨，
hán　méi　zuì　kān　hèn

长　作　去　年　花。
cháng　zuò　qù　nián　huā

① 定定：安定，安稳的样子。住：一作"任"。
② 依依：隐约。物华：自然景色。

第十三单元

lóu gé tíng tǎ
楼 阁 亭 塔

zhāng xiàng yáng
◎ 张 向 阳

nǐ shuō lóu wǒ shuō lóu
你 说 楼，我 说 楼，

běi jīng zǐ jìn chéng jiǎo lóu
北 京 紫 禁 城 角 楼，

yún nán kūn míng dà guān lóu
云 南 昆 明 大 观 楼，

hú běi wǔ chāng huáng hè lóu
湖 北 武 昌 黄 鹤 楼。

nǐ shuō gé wǒ shuō gé
你 说 阁，我 说 阁，

jiāng xī nán chāng téng wáng gé
江 西 南 昌 滕 王 阁，

zhè jiāng níng bō tiān yī gé
浙 江 宁 波 天 一 阁，

shān dōng péng lái yǒu xiān gé
山 东 蓬 莱 有 仙 阁。

nǐ shuō tíng wǒ shuō tíng
你 说 亭，我 说 亭，

hú nán cháng shā ài wǎn tíng
湖 南 长 沙 爱 晚 亭，

háng zhōu xī hú hú xīn tíng
杭 州 西 湖 湖 心 亭，

lǔ xùn gù xiāng yǒu lán tíng
鲁 迅 故 乡 有 兰 亭。

nǐ shuō tǎ wǒ shuō tǎ
你 说 塔，我 说 塔，

jiāng sū sū zhōu hǔ qiū tǎ
江 苏 苏 州 虎 丘 塔，

ān huī ān qìng zhèn fēng tǎ
安 徽 安 庆 振 风 塔，

shǎn xī xī ān dà yàn tǎ
陕 西 西 安 大 雁 塔。

xiǎo xiǎo jiǎo yā zǒu tiān xià
小 小 脚 丫 走 天 下，

lóu gé tíng tǎ dài huí jiā
楼 阁 亭 塔 带 回 家。

tiào
跳

[英 国]米尔恩

有只知更鸟去了，

跳呀，跳呀，

跳呀，跳呀，跳。

无论如何我要告诉它：

走路别这么跳呀跳。

它说它不能停止跳，

如果它停止跳，

它就啥地方也去不了。

可爱的知更鸟，

nà jiù shá dì fang yě qù bù liǎo
那 就 啥 地 方 也 去 不 了……

zhè jiù shì wèi shá tā zǒu lù
这 就 是 为 啥 它 走 路

zǒng shì tiào ya tiào ya tiào ya
总 是 跳 呀，跳 呀，跳 呀，

tiào ya tiào ya
跳 呀，跳 呀，

tiào ya
跳 呀，

tiào
跳。

lóu fēi fǔ yì
（楼 飞 甫 译）

这是一首会跳的诗，你看，知更鸟在跳；你看，音节在跳，字字句句在跳。你感觉到了吗？这是一个跳动的世界。

树

[日本]金子美铃

花谢了
果熟了，

果子落下来
叶子掉光了，

然后又发芽，

开花。

就这样
要重复多少次，
这棵树
才可以歇息呢？

（吴菲 译）

鱼儿睡在哪里

[苏联] 托克玛科娃

夜里很黑。夜里静悄悄。

鱼儿,鱼儿,你在哪里睡觉?

狐狸往洞里躲。

狗钻进了自己的窝。

松鼠溜进了树洞。

老鼠溜进了地洞。

可是,河里,水面,

哪儿也找不到你的身影。

hēi gu lōng dōng de jìng qiāo qiāo de
黑咕隆咚的,静悄悄的,

yú er yú er nǐ shuì zài nǎ er
鱼儿,鱼儿,你睡在哪儿?

wéi wéi yì
(韦苇 译)

赏析

黑咕隆咚的夜里,让小朋友充满了好奇与疑问:鱼儿们,夜里睡在哪里呢?已知的经验和未知的探询,让我们读出孩子对世界的追问。

wèn liú shí jiǔ
问 刘 十 九 ①

táng bái jū yì
（唐）白 居 易

lǜ yǐ xīn pēi jiǔ
绿 蚁 新 醅 酒 ②，

hóng ní xiǎo huǒ lú
红 泥 小 火 炉 。

wǎn lái tiān yù xuě
晚 来 天 欲 雪 ，

néng yǐn yì bēi wú
能 饮 一 杯 无 ③？

① 刘十九：嵩阳人，名不详，十九是排行。

② 绿蚁：新酿成尚未过滤的酒，因酒渣如蚁，略呈绿色，故称。醅：未经过滤的酒。

③ 无：疑问词，同"可否"的"否"。

第十四单元

huáng hé yáo
黄 河 谣

◎ mín jiān tóng yáo
◎ 民 间 童 谣

tiān xià huáng hé jǐ dào wān 天 下 黄 河 几 道 湾？	tiān xià huáng hé jiǔ dào wān 天 下 黄 河 九 道 湾，
jǐ dào zhǎi lái jǐ dào kuān 几 道 窄 来 几 道 宽？	tóu dào zhǎi lái èr dào kuān 头 道 窄 来 二 道 宽。
jǐ dào wān li néng pǎo mǎ 几 道 湾 里 能 跑 马？	sān dào wān li néng pǎo mǎ 三 道 湾 里 能 跑 马，
jǐ dào wān li néng xíng chuán 几 道 湾 里 能 行 船？	sì dào wān li néng xíng chuán 四 道 湾 里 能 行 船。
jǐ dào wān li chū bǎo bèi 几 道 湾 里 出 宝 贝？	wǔ dào wān li chū bǎo bèi 五 道 湾 里 出 宝 贝，
jǐ dào wān li lǎo lóng tán 几 道 湾 里 老 龙 潭？	liù dào wān li lǎo lóng tán 六 道 湾 里 老 龙 潭。
jǐ dào wān li yǔ wáng miào 几 道 湾 里 禹 王 庙？	qī dào wān li yǔ wáng miào 七 道 湾 里 禹 王 庙，
jǐ dào wān li guò bā xiān 几 道 湾 里 过 八 仙？	bā dào wān li guò bā xiān 八 道 湾 里 过 八 仙。
jǐ dào wān li tōng tiān hé 几 道 湾 里 通 天 河？	jiǔ dào wān li tōng tiān hé 九 道 湾 里 通 天 河，
tiān lián dì jiē jǐ wàn nián 天 连 地 接 几 万 年？	tiān lián dì jiē jiǔ wàn nián 天 连 地 接 九 万 年。

tài yáng
太　　阳

[塞内加尔] B.迪奥普

huáng huáng de tài yáng
黄　黄　的　太　阳
guāng liū liū de tài yáng
光　溜　溜　的　太　阳
xiè xià jīn sè de bō guāng
泻　下　金　色　的　波　光
fú xiàn zài huáng sè de
浮　现　在　黄　色　的
hé miàn shang
河　面　上

bái bái de tài yáng
白　白　的　太　阳
guāng liū liū de tài yáng
光　溜　溜　的　太　阳
xiè xià yín sè de bō guāng
泻　下　银　色　的　波　光

fú dòng zài bái sè de
浮　动　在　白　色　的
hé miàn shang
河　面　上

hóng hóng de tài yáng
红　红　的　太　阳
guāng liū liū de tài yáng
光　溜　溜　的　太　阳
xiè xià xuè sè de bō guāng
泻　下　血　色　的　波　光
yáo luò zài hóng sè de
摇　落　在　红　色　的
hé miàn shang
河　面　上

zhōu guó yǒng yì
（周　国　勇　译）

赏析

　　不同颜色的太阳，就像给小河涂上了厚厚的油彩，给我们展现了绚烂而多彩的自然景致。整齐的节奏，浓烈的色调，展示了诗歌的魅力。

xiào shēng
笑 声

mǎ lái xī yà liáng zhì qìng
[马 来 西 亚] 梁 志 庆

xià kè zhōng shēng xiǎng hòu
下课钟声响后,
xiào shēng yě jiù xiǎng le
笑声也就响了,
tā guà mǎn jiào shì
它挂满教室,
chuàn zài zǒu láng shang
串在走廊上,
rán hòu tiào xià tī jí
然后跳下梯级,
yuè yuǎn shēng yīn yuè xì
越远,声音越细。

xiào shēng
笑声,
zhuī zhú zài cāo chǎng shang
追逐在操场上,

gěi zhuā zhù de xiào shēng
给抓住的笑声,
yòu hé jǐ gè xiào shēng
又和几个笑声,
niǔ chéng yì tuán
扭成一团,
fēn bù kāi lái le
分不开来了。

shàng kè zhōng shēng yì xiǎng
上课钟声一响,
xiào shēng jiù hé jiě le
笑声就和解了。
zǒu jìn jiào shì hòu de tóng xué men
走进教室后的同学们,
zài yě bú luàn diū xiào shēng le
再也不乱丢笑声了!

赏析　　课间是孩子们欢笑的时间,是游戏的时间。作者用笑声来替代那一群活泼泼的孩子,笑声在行动,笑声在游戏。这是一首构思巧妙、形象生动的童诗。

bù xué xiě zì yǒu huài chù
不 学 写 字 有 坏 处

zhōng guó tái wān　fāng sù zhēn
（ 中 国 台 湾 ） 方 素 珍

xiǎo chóng xiě xìn gěi mǎ yǐ
小 虫 写 信 给 蚂 蚁

tā zài yè zi shang
他 在 叶 子 上

yǎo le sān gè dòng
咬 了 三 个 洞

biǎo shì wǒ xiǎng nǐ
表 示 我 想 你

mǎ yǐ shōu dào tā de xìn
蚂 蚁 收 到 他 的 信

yě zài yè zi shang
也 在 叶 子 上

yǎo le sān gè dòng
咬 了 三 个 洞

biǎo shì kàn bù dǒng
表 示 看 不 懂

xiǎo chóng bù zhī dào mǎ yǐ
小 虫 不 知 道 蚂 蚁

de yì si
的 意 思

mǎ yǐ bù zhī dào xiǎo chóng
蚂 蚁 不 知 道 小 虫

de xiǎng niàn
的 想 念

zěn me bàn ne
怎 么 办 呢?

赏析　　小虫和蚂蚁都在叶子上咬了三个洞,表示不同的意思,可是对方却看不懂。怎么办呢? 从而引出诗题——不学写字有坏处。在饶有趣味的童话诗里蕴含着一个沟通的问题,让人深受启发。

81

jīng xuě
惊 雪

táng lù chàng
（唐）陆 畅

guài dé běi fēng jí
怪 得 北 风 急 ①，

qián tíng rú yuè huī
前 庭 如 月 辉。

tiān rén nìng xǔ qiǎo
天 人 宁 许 巧 ②，

jiǎn shuǐ zuò huā fēi
剪 水 作 花 飞。

注释

① 怪得：奇怪，怎么。
② 宁：岂，难道。

第十五单元

shí shǔ duì huā yáo
十 数 对 花 谣

mín jiān tóng yáo
◎ 民 间 童 谣

wǒ shuō yī shéi duì yī
我 说 一,谁 对 一,
shén me kāi huā zài shuǐ li
什 么 开 花 在 水 里?
nǐ shuō yī wǒ duì yī
你 说 一,我 对 一,
líng jiao kāi huā zài shuǐ li
菱 角 开 花 在 水 里!

wǒ shuō èr shéi duì èr
我 说 二,谁 对 二,
shén me kāi huā bǎ dào yán
什 么 开 花 把 道 沿?
nǐ shuō èr wǒ duì èr
你 说 二,我 对 二,
mǎ lán kāi huā bǎ dào yán
马 兰 开 花 把 道 沿!

wǒ shuō sān shéi duì sān
我 说 三,谁 对 三,

shén me kāi huā yè yè jiān
什 么 开 花 叶 叶 尖?
nǐ shuō sān wǒ duì sān
你 说 三,我 对 三,
jiǔ cài kāi huā yè yè jiān
韭 菜 开 花 叶 叶 尖!

wǒ shuō sì shéi duì sì
我 说 四,谁 对 四,
shén me kāi huā yì shēn cì
什 么 开 花 一 身 刺?
nǐ shuō sì wǒ duì sì
你 说 四,我 对 四,
huáng guā kāi huā yì shēn cì
黄 瓜 开 花 一 身 刺!

wǒ shuō wǔ shéi duì wǔ
我 说 五,谁 对 五,
shén me kāi huā zài duān wǔ
什 么 开 花 在 端 午?

nǐ shuō wǔ wǒ duì wǔ
你 说 五，我 对 五，
hú lu kāi huā wǔ yuè wǔ
葫 芦 开 花 五 月 五！

wǒ shuō liù shéi duì liù
我 说 六，谁 对 六，
shén me kāi huā yì shēn ròu
什 么 开 花 一 身 肉？
nǐ shuō liù wǒ duì liù
你 说 六，我 对 六，
qié zi kāi huā yì shēn ròu
茄 子 开 花 一 身 肉！

wǒ shuō qī shéi duì qī
我 说 七，谁 对 七，
shén me kāi huā bǎ tóu dī
什 么 开 花 把 头 低？
nǐ shuō qī wǒ duì qī
你 说 七，我 对 七，
kuí huā kāi huā bǎ tóu dī
葵 花 开 花 把 头 低！

wǒ shuō bā shéi duì bā
我 说 八，谁 对 八，

shén me kāi huā hú zi lā chā
什 么 开 花 胡 子 拉 碴？
nǐ shuō bā wǒ duì bā
你 说 八，我 对 八，
bāo mǐ kāi huā hú zi lā chā
苞 米 开 花 胡 子 拉 碴！

wǒ shuō jiǔ shéi duì jiǔ
我 说 九，谁 对 九，
shén me kāi huā jiā jiā yǒu
什 么 开 花 家 家 有？
nǐ shuō jiǔ wǒ duì jiǔ
你 说 九，我 对 九，
dì dòu kāi huā jiā jiā yǒu
地 豆 开 花 家 家 有！

wǒ shuō shí shéi duì shí
我 说 十，谁 对 十，
shén me kāi huā suí bò ji
什 么 开 花 随 簸 箕？
nǐ shuō shí wǒ duì shí
你 说 十，我 对 十，
sào zhou kāi huā suí bò ji
扫 帚 开 花 随 簸 箕！

yuè liang shòu le yì diǎn
月 亮 瘦 了 一 点

zhōng guó tái wān wū bǎo líng
（中 国 台 湾 ）巫 宝 玲

yǒu yí gè gān jìng de shuǐ kēng
有 一 个 干 净 的 水 坑

lǐ miàn yǒu yí gè yuè liang
里 面 有 一 个 月 亮

wǒ yòng lì yì cǎi
我 用 力 一 踩

yuè liang suí zhe shuǐ huā fēi chu qu
月 亮 随 着 水 花 飞 出 去

kě shì děng shuǐ píng jìng hòu
可 是 等 水 平 静 后

yuè liang hái shì zài nà er
月 亮 还 是 在 那 儿

zhǐ shì shòu le yì diǎn
只 是 瘦 了 一 点

xīng yuè de lái yóu
星 月 的 来 由

gù chéng
◎ 顾 城

shù zhī xiǎng qù sī liè tiān kōng
树枝 想 去 撕 裂 天 空,

dàn què zhǐ chuō le jǐ gè wēi xiǎo de kū long
但 却 只 戳 了 几 个 微 小 的 窟 窿,

tā tòu chū le tiān wài de guāng liàng
它 透 出 了 天 外 的 光 亮,

rén men bǎ tā jiào zuò yuè liang hé xīng xing
人 们 把 它 叫 作 月 亮 和 星 星。

　　月亮和星星从哪里来,每个孩子都有自己的理解。诗人却理解为树想撕裂天空,只戳了几个窟窿。真是一首"异想天开"的诗歌。

dōng yé ye niē hóng le dì di de bí zi
冬爷爷捏红了弟弟的鼻子

lǐ kūn chún
◎李昆纯

tiān kōng zhōng
天空中

yì duǒ duǒ xuě huā
一朵朵雪花

zài piāo
在飘……

běi fēng li
北风里，

yì zhī zhī è niǎo
一只只饿鸟

zài jiào
在叫……

dà shù xià
大树下，

dì di jǔ qǐ dàn gōng
弟弟举起弹弓

zài miáo
在瞄……

rě nǎo le dōng yé ye
惹恼了冬爷爷，

bǎ dì di de xiǎo bí zi
把弟弟的小鼻子

niē hóng le
捏红了。

赏析　北风里，一只只饿鸟在叫，真叫人同情。可调皮的弟弟却举起弹弓，瞄准了饿鸟……难怪冬爷爷生气了。读了这样的诗，是不是也让小朋友们有了一些启发、一点思考呢？

夜　雪

（唐）白居易

已讶衾枕冷①，
复见窗户明。
夜深知雪重，
时闻折竹声②。

① 讶：惊奇，奇怪。衾枕：被褥枕头。
② 折竹声：指竹子被大雪压断的声音。

第十六单元

dà nián chū yī niǔ yì niǔ
大年初一扭一扭

mín jiān tóng yáo
◎ 民间童谣

xiǎo hái er xiǎo hái er
小孩儿，小孩儿，

nǐ bié chán
你别馋，

guò le là bā jiù shì nián
过了腊八就是年。

là bā zhōu er hē jǐ tiān
腊八粥儿喝几天，

lī li lā lā èr shí sān
哩哩啦啦二十三。

èr shí sān táng guā er nián
二十三，糖瓜儿黏，

èr shí sì sǎo wū zi
二十四，扫屋子，

èr shí wǔ hú chuāng hu
二十五，糊窗户，

èr shí liù zhǔ zhu ròu
二十六，煮煮肉，

èr shí qī zǎi gōng jī
二十七，宰公鸡，

èr shí bā bǎ miàn fā
二十八，把面发，

èr shí jiǔ zhēng mán tou
二十九，蒸馒头，

sān shí er wǎn shang áo yì xiǔ
三十儿晚上熬一宿，

dà nián chū yī niǔ yì niǔ
大年初一扭一扭。

mèi mei de hóng yǔ xié
妹妹的红雨鞋

zhōng guó tái wān　　lín huàn zhāng
（中国台湾）林焕彰

mèi mei de hóng yǔ xié
妹妹的红雨鞋，

shì xīn mǎi de
是新买的。

xià yǔ tiān
下雨天，

tā zuì xǐ huan chuān zhe
她最喜欢穿着

dào wū wài qù yóu xì
到屋外去游戏，

wǒ xǐ huan duǒ zài
我喜欢躲在

wū zi li
屋子里，

gé zhe bō li chuāng kàn tā men
隔着玻璃窗看它们

yóu lái yóu qù
游 来 游 去

xiàng yú gāng li de yí duì
像 鱼 缸 里 的 一 对

hóng jīn yú
红 金 鱼。

"游来游去的红金鱼",多鲜亮的色彩呀！让下雨天也美丽
起来,快乐起来。红艳艳的新雨鞋给灰蒙蒙的雨天带来了亮色。
这是一首美丽的小诗。

给小懒惰画个像

gěi xiǎo lǎn duò huà gè xiàng

rén róng róng
◎ 任 溶 溶

从 前 有 个 小 懒 惰，
cóng qián yǒu gè xiǎo lǎn duò

爱 把 懒 话 说。
ài bǎ lǎn huà shuō

穿 件 衣 服 很 简 单，
chuān jiàn yī fu hěn jiǎn dān

他 说 麻 烦 多：
tā shuō má fan duō

"早 晨 起 来 得 穿 上 ，
zǎo chen qǐ lai děi chuān shang

晚 上 又 得 脱；
wǎn shang yòu děi tuō

天 热 衣 服 得 减 少，
tiān rè yī fu děi jiǎn shǎo

天 冷 得 加 多。
tiān lěng děi jiā duō

要 是 身 上 长 了 毛，
yào shì shēn shang zhǎng le máo

那，那，多 快 活……
nà nà duō kuài huo

还 有 吃 饭 也 麻 烦，
hái yǒu chī fàn yě má fan

shāo fàn děi shēng huǒ
烧 饭 得 生 火，

chī le hái děi xǐ wǎn kuài
吃 了 还 得 洗 碗 筷，

hái yào shuā fàn guō
还 要 刷 饭 锅！

gān cuì zhù zài shù shang mian
干 脆 住 在 树 上 面，

è le chī shuǐ guǒ
饿 了 吃 水 果。

zhǐ yào zhuǎ zi zhuā lái chī
只 要 爪 子 抓 来 吃，

shǒu yě yòng bù zháo
手 也 用 不 着。

gān cuì zhǎng tiáo dà wěi ba
干 脆 长 条 大 尾 巴，

zhǐ yào bǎ shù bō
只 要 把 树 拨，

shuǐ guǒ zì jǐ diào xia lai
水 果 自 己 掉 下 来，

zhí wǎng zuǐ li luò
直 往 嘴 里 落……"

wǒ lái gěi tā huà gè xiàng
我 来 给 他 画 个 像，

jiù zhào tā suǒ shuō
就 照 他 所 说，

qǐng dà jiā lái kàn yí kàn
请 大 家 来 看 一 看：

tā ya xiàng shén me
他 呀 像 什 么？

máo jīn
毛 巾

zhōng guó tái wān　xiè wǔ zhāng
（中 国 台 湾 ）谢 武 彰

liàn xí bù de liǎn zāng le
练 习 簿 的 脸 脏 了

xiàng pí cā zi shì máo jīn
橡 皮 擦 子 是 毛 巾

bǎ tā de liǎn xǐ gān jìng
把 他 的 脸 洗 干 净

dà hēi bǎn de liǎn zāng le
大 黑 板 的 脸 脏 了

hēi bǎn cā zi shì máo jīn
黑 板 擦 子 是 毛 巾

bǎ tā de liǎn xǐ gān jìng
把 他 的 脸 洗 干 净

xiǎo pí xié de liǎn zāng le
小 皮 鞋 的 脸 脏 了

pí xié shuā zi shì máo jīn
皮 鞋 刷 子 是 毛 巾

bǎ tā de liǎn xǐ gān jìng
把 他 的 脸 洗 干 净

wǒ de liǎn yě zāng le
我 的 脸 也 脏 了

yí   máo jīn zhēn táo qì
咦？毛 巾 真 淘 气

duǒ dào nǎ li qù le
躲 到 哪 里 去 了？

赏析　日常生活中的事物在诗人笔下，有了更多的内涵。橡皮擦子是毛巾，黑板擦子是毛巾……思路一打开，缤纷的想象就会纷至沓来，还有什么东西是毛巾呢？

十二月十五夜
shí èr yuè shí wǔ yè

（清）袁 枚
qīng yuán méi

沉 沉 更 鼓 急 ①，
chén chén gēng gǔ jí

渐 渐 人 声 绝。
jiàn jiàn rén shēng jué

吹 灯 窗 更 明，
chuī dēng chuāng gèng míng

月 照 一 天 雪。
yuè zhào yì tiān xuě

注释

① 沉沉：深沉。更鼓：夜晚报更的鼓。更，古代一夜分为五更，每更大约两小时。

下

卷

第一单元

chén dú duì yùn yī
晨 读 对 韵（一）

má
麻（a）

tiān duì dì shì duì jiā luò rì duì liú xiá
天 对 地，室 对 家，落 日 对 流 霞。

huáng yīng duì cuì niǎo tián cài duì kǔ guā
黄 莺 对 翠 鸟，甜 菜 对 苦 瓜。

gǒu wěi cǎo jī guān huā
狗 尾 草，鸡 冠 花。

bái lù duì wū yā
白 鹭 对 乌 鸦。

mén qián zāi guǒ shù táng li yǎng yú xiā
门 前 栽 果 树，塘 里 养 鱼 虾。

yǒu shí sān diǎn liǎng diǎn yǔ dào chù shí zhī wǔ zhī huā
有 时 三 点 两 点 雨，到 处 十 枝 五 枝 花。

晨 读 对 韵 （二）

麻（a）

优对劣，丑对佳，肃静对喧哗。

光明对黑暗，谨慎对浮夸。

瓜子脸，葡萄牙①。

异卉对奇葩。

知己存海内，朋友遍天涯。

黄梅时节家家雨，

青草池塘处处蛙。

① 葡萄牙：国名，"瓜子"对"葡萄"，"脸"对"牙"，这是一个无情对（对联方式的一种变格）。

100

xiǎo huā hé xiǎo cǎo
小 花 和 小 草

◎ hán zhì liàng
◎ 韩 志 亮

yì zhū xiǎo cǎo
一 株 小 草，

kāi chū yì duǒ xiǎo huā
开 出 一 朵 小 花。

zhè ge wèn tí yǒu diǎn má fan
这 个 问 题 有 点 麻 烦！

wǒ men yì qǐ shāng liang yí xià
我 们 一 起 商 量 一 下：

xiàn zài kāi shǐ
现 在 开 始，

hǎn tā xiǎo huā
喊 她 小 花，

hái shì xiǎo cǎo
还 是 小 草？

赏析　　春天里，每一棵小草的生长，每一朵小花的盛开都会给大自然带来生机，给孩子们带来快乐。瞧，小草上开放了一朵小花，喊她是小花还是小草呢？就成了一个问题。虽然有一点点麻烦，可是我们却读出了几分欣喜。

bào zhú
爆　竹

niú bō
◎ 牛 波

bào zhú
爆 竹

nǐ yì shēng zhǐ shuō yí jù huà
你 一 生 只 说 一 句 话

nǐ zài hái zi de shǒu shang shuō
你 在 孩 子 的 手 上 说

nǐ zài cháng cháng de zhú gān
你 在 长 长 的 竹 竿

shang shuō
上 说

yǒu shí nǐ lián zhe chuàn shuō
有 时 你 连 着 串 说

yǒu shí nǐ fēi shàng tiān qù shuō
有 时 你 飞 上 天 去 说

wú lùn nǐ zěn me shuō
无 论 你 怎 么 说

dà shēng shuō xiǎo shēng shuō
大 声 说 小 声 说

bù guǎn lǎo yé ye hé xiǎo sūn sun
不 管 老 爷 爷 和 小 孙 孙

dōu xǐ ài tīng nǐ shuō
都 喜 爱 听 你 说

rén men shuō bù chū de kuài lè
人 们 说 不 出 的 快 乐

nǐ yí jù huà jiù shuō le
你 一 句 话 就 说 了

赏析　　　人们在喜庆的日子里都喜欢放爆竹庆祝。爆竹的话会把我们带进喜庆的气氛中。特别是最后一节，语言简洁，意蕴深刻，让人不由得会心一笑。

dù hàn jiāng
渡 汉 江

táng sòng zhī wèn
（唐）宋 之 问

líng wài yīn shū duàn
岭 外 音 书 断①，

jīng dōng fù lì chūn
经 冬 复 历 春。

jìn xiāng qíng gèng qiè
近 乡 情 更 怯②，

bù gǎn wèn lái rén
不 敢 问 来 人③。

① 岭外：即岭南。岭，指大庾（yǔ）岭。

② 怯：胆怯，心情紧张。

③ 来人：指来自家乡、熟悉诗人家里情况的人。

第二单元

chén dú duì yùn sān
晨 读 对 韵（三）

bō
波（o）

fán duì jiǎn shǎo duì duō xī lì duì pāng tuó
繁对简，少对多，淅沥对滂沱。

shān hú duì mǎ nǎo hé bàng duì tián luó
珊瑚对玛瑙，河蚌对田螺。

xīng wǔ mèi yuè pó suō
星妩媚，月婆娑。

qū jìng duì xié pō
曲径对斜坡。

huáng lí gē wǎn zhuǎn lǜ liǔ wǔ ē nuó
黄鹂歌婉转①，绿柳舞婀娜②。

fāng lín xīn yè cuī chén yè
芳林新叶催陈叶，

liú shuǐ qián bō ràng hòu bō
流水前波让后波。

注释

① 婉转：形容声音抑扬顿挫，十分动听。

② 婀娜：姿态轻柔美好。

晨读对韵（四）

波（o）

弦对管，鼓对锣，守卫对巡逻。

观光对借鉴，视察对观摩。

须奋斗，莫蹉跎①。

北海对东坡②。

眼中沧海小，衣上白云多③。

气似长虹贯玉宇，

心如皓月映澄波④。

① 蹉跎：虚度光阴。

② 北海：汉代孔融为北海令，人称孔北海。东坡：宋代大诗人苏轼，在黄冈东坡筑室，因号东坡。

③ 为福建鼓山楹联。

④ 转引自王尚文、叶柏青编著的《对韵新编》。

wǒ lái le
我 来 了

◎ 张 秋 生
zhāng qiū shēng

chūn tiān yòng dì yī gè xiǎo nèn yá
春 天，用 第 一 个 小 嫩 芽

shuō wǒ lái le
说：我 来 了。

xià tiān yòng dì yī gè xiǎo huā lěi
夏 天，用 第 一 个 小 花 蕾

shuō wǒ lái le
说：我 来 了。

qiū tiān yòng dì yī zhāng piāo luò de yè
秋 天，用 第 一 张 飘 落 的 叶

shuō wǒ lái le
说：我 来 了。

dōng tiān yòng dì yī duǒ jié bái de xuě huā
冬 天，用 第 一 朵 洁 白 的 雪 花

shuō wǒ lái le
说：我 来 了。

赏析　　四季躲在哪里？一个嫩芽，一个花蕾，一张落叶，一朵雪花都会告诉你。全诗采用了拟人的手法，构式工整，易于诵读。

lǎo shǔ xiù zhe yóu dòu xiāng
老 鼠 嗅 着 油 豆 香

◎ mín jiān tóng yáo
◎ 民 间 童 谣

yóu yì gāng
油一缸，

dòu yì kuāng
豆一筐，

lǎo shǔ xiù zhe yóu dòu xiāng
老鼠嗅着油豆香。

pá shàng gāng
爬上缸，

tiào jìn kuāng
跳进筐，

tōu yóu tōu dòu liǎng tóu máng
偷油偷豆两头忙。

yòu gāo xìng
又高兴，

yòu huāng zhāng
又慌张，

jiǎo yì huá
脚 一 滑，

shēn yí huàng
身 一 晃，

pū tōng yì shēng diē jìn gāng
"扑 通" 一 声 跌 进 缸。

赏析　　在童谣里，小老鼠的形象总是给人们带来欢笑。瞧，这只小老鼠又要偷油又要偷豆，忙得不亦乐乎。童谣用三七句式风趣地描绘了这一场景，在变幻的节奏中给我们带来阅读的快乐。

féng xuě sù fú róng shān zhǔ rén
逢 雪 宿 芙 蓉 山 主 人

táng liú cháng qīng
（唐）刘 长 卿

rì mù cāng shān yuǎn
日 暮 苍 山 远 ①,

tiān hán bái wū pín
天 寒 白 屋 贫 ②。

chái mén wén quǎn fèi
柴 门 闻 犬 吠 ③,

fēng xuě yè guī rén
风 雪 夜 归 人。

注释

① 苍山：青色的山。

② 白屋：贫苦人家所住的茅草屋子，以白茅覆盖，所以叫"白屋"。

③ 柴门：篱笆门。吠：狗叫。

第三单元

chén dú duì yùn wǔ
晨 读 对 韵（五）

gē
歌（e）

píng duì zǎo jú duì hé huáng dòu duì qīng kē
萍 对 藻，菊 对 荷，黄 豆 对 青 稞。

táo zhī duì liǔ yè fàng hè duì guān é
桃 枝 对 柳 叶，放 鹤 对 观 鹅。

xiǎo yè qǔ dà fēng gē
小 夜 曲，大 风 歌①。

liàn yàn duì cuó é
激 滟 对 嵯 峨②。

jǔ tóu hóng rì jìn huí shǒu bái yún zhē
举 头 红 日 近，回 首 白 云 遮。

zuò dì rì xíng bā wàn lǐ xún tiān yáo kàn yì qiān hé
坐 地 日 行 八 万 里，巡 天 遥 看 一 千 河。

注释
　　① 大风歌：汉高祖刘邦平定天下后回到家乡沛县，感慨万千而唱《大风歌》。
　　② 激滟：形容水波荡漾。嵯峨：形容山势高峻。

chén dú duì yùn liù
晨 读 对 韵（六）

gē
歌（e）

qín duì lǎn jiǎn duì shē suǒ suì duì fán kē
勤 对 懒，俭 对 奢，琐 碎 对 繁 苛。

bīng qīng duì yù rùn dì lì duì rén hé
冰 清 对 玉 润，地 利 对 人 和。

xíng jǔ jǔ xiào hē hē
行 踽 踽，笑 呵 呵。

xīn shǎng duì yín é
欣 赏 对 吟 哦。

xià bǐ jí qiān zì dú shū qīng wǔ chē
下 笔 即 千 字，读 书 倾 五 车。

shēng yǒu guāng huī zhào rì yuè
生 有 光 辉 照 日 月，

sǐ liú zhèng qì zhuàng shān hé
死 留 正 气 壮 山 河。

chūn tiān zài nǎ li
春 天 在 哪 里

zhōng guó tái wān   xiè wǔ zhāng
（ 中 国 台 湾 ）谢 武 彰

fēng pǎo de zhí chuǎn qì
风 跑 得 直 喘 气

xiàng dà jiā bào gào hǎo xiāo xi
向 大 家 报 告 好 消 息：

chūn tiān lái le
春 天 来 了——

chūn tiān lái le
春 天 来 了——

huā duǒ men tīng jian le
花 朵 们 听 见 了

dōu zhàn zài zhī tóu shang
都 站 在 枝 头 上

lái huān yíng chūn tiān
来 欢 迎 春 天

děng le hǎo jiǔ hǎo jiǔ
等 了 好 久 好 久

hái shì kàn bú jiàn
还 是 看 不 见

dōu jí de diǎn qǐ jiǎo jiān
都 急 得 踮 起 脚 尖

hù xiāng wèn zhe shuō
互 相 问 着 说：

chūn tiān zài nǎ li
春 天 在 哪 里？

chūn tiān zài nǎ li
春 天 在 哪 里？

huā bù zhī dào zì jǐ jiù
花，不 知 道 自 己 就

shì chūn tiān
是 春 天。

赏析　　从风儿的喘气相告，到花儿踮脚寻找，读来一气呵成，饶有趣味。寻找春天的花儿，不知道自己就是春天，这样的构思真是奇妙！

bā shí bā zhī bā ge niǎo

八十八只八哥鸟

mín jiān tóng yáo
◎ 民 间 童 谣

bā shí bā lǎo ye jiā mén kǒu yǒu bā shí bā zhī dà máo zhú
八十八老爷家门口有八十八枝大毛竹,

yǒu bā shí bā zhī bā ge yāo qiú dào bā shí bā lǎo ye jiā mén kǒu
有八十八只八哥要求到八十八老爷家门口

bā shí bā zhī dà máo zhú shang zhù bā shí bā gè bā ge wō
八十八枝大毛竹上筑八十八个八哥窝。

bā shí bā lǎo ye bù tóng yì bā shí bā zhī bā ge zài tā jiā mén kǒu
八十八老爷不同意八十八只八哥在他家门口

bā shí bā zhī dà máo zhú shang zhù bā shí bā gè bā ge wō
八十八枝大毛竹上筑八十八个八哥窝,

bā shí bā zhī bā ge kǔ kǔ āi qiú bā shí bā lǎo ye kāi ēn
八十八只八哥苦苦哀求八十八老爷开恩,

dā ying tā men zài bā shí bā zhī dà máo zhú shang zhù bā
答应它们在八十八枝大毛竹上筑八

shí bā gè bā ge wō
十八个八哥窝。

赏析　这是一首绕口令。围绕着八十八老爷、八十八枝大毛竹、八十八只八哥进行着语言的游戏。阅读时可以从慢到快,让孩子体会到逐步提升,直到熟练诵读的乐趣。

绝 句

（唐）杜甫

迟日江山丽①，
春风花草香。
泥融飞燕子②，
沙暖睡鸳鸯。

注释

① 迟日：指春天的太阳。
② "泥融"句：春泥黏湿，故燕子衔泥筑巢频飞。

第四单元

chén dú duì yùn qī
晨 读 对 韵（七）

zhī
支（-i）

tíng duì yuàn jǐng duì chí luò xù duì yóu sī
庭 对 院，井 对 池，落 絮 对 游 丝。

fēi qín duì zǒu shòu jùn mǎ duì xióng shī
飞 禽 对 走 兽，骏 马 对 雄 狮。

sān guó zhì qī bù shī
三 国 志，七 步 诗。

cuò luò duì cēn cī
错 落 对 参 差。

xíng dào shuǐ qióng chù zuò kàn yún qǐ shí
行 到 水 穷 处，坐 看 云 起 时。

cè shēn tiān dì gèng huái gǔ
侧 身 天 地 更 怀 古，

dú lì cāng máng zì yǒng shī
独 立 苍 茫 自 咏 诗①。

注释

①为成都杜甫草堂东展览室楹联，谢无量作，集自杜甫诗句。

115

chén dú duì yùn bā
晨 读 对 韵（八）

zhī
支（-i）

xíng duì zhǐ shàn duì cí běn xìng duì tiān zī
行 对 止，善 对 慈，本 性 对 天 资。

cū xīn duì dà dǎn yì yǒu duì liáng shī
粗 心 对 大 胆，益 友 对 良 师。

sūn xíng zhě   zǔ chōng zhī
孙 行 者 ①，祖 冲 之 ②。

lǔ xùn duì xú chí
鲁 迅 对 徐 迟 ③。

bǐ sǎo lóng shé zì   xiōng cáng jǐn xiù cí
笔 扫 龙 蛇 字 ④，胸 藏 锦 绣 词。

piān duō rè xuè piān duō gǔ
偏 多 热 血 偏 多 骨，

bù huǐ zhēn qíng bù huǐ chī
不 悔 真 情 不 悔 痴。

注释

① 孙行者：孙悟空。
② 祖冲之：我国古代数学家，发现了圆周率。
③ 徐迟：当代作家、翻译家。
④ 龙蛇字：比喻笔势蜿蜒洒脱的草书。

yún
云

rì běn jīn zǐ měi líng
[日本] 金子美铃

wǒ xiǎng biàn chéng
我 想 变 成
yì duǒ yún
一 朵 云。

yòu sōng yòu ruǎn
又 松 又 软
piāo zài lán tiān li
飘 在 蓝 天 里,
cóng zhè tóu dào nà tóu
从 这 头 到 那 头
kàn gòu le fēng jǐng
看 够 了 风 景,
wǎn shang jiù gēn yuè liang
晚 上 就 跟 月 亮

zhuō mí cáng
捉 迷 藏。

wán nì le
玩 腻 了
jiù biàn chéng yǔ
就 变 成 雨,
gēn léi gōng
跟 雷 公
jié gè bàn
结 个 伴,
yì qǐ tiào jìn
一 起 跳 进
rén jiā de chí táng li qu
人 家 的 池 塘 里 去。

wú fēi yì
(吴 菲 译)

赏析　自由自在的云多好,在天上玩够了,还可以跳到人家的池塘里去。在诗里,我们可以读出孩子对自由自在的生活的向往。

117

chūn tiān lái
春 天 来

◎ 薛 卫 民

春天来，雁打头，
冬雪化，冰水流。
鸭鹅天上瞅一瞅，
摇摇摆摆河里走。

春天来，风打头，
摇着树，赶着牛。
耕田耕到西山口，
小孩送饭领条狗。

赏析 春天来了，大自然有哪些变化呢？冬雪融化，新芽萌发，充满了朝气。瞧，耕牛又开始劳作了，一段新的旅程又开始了，你准备好了吗？

忆东山二首（其一）①
yì dōng shān èr shǒu qí yī

（唐）李白
táng lǐ bái

不向东山久，
bú xiàng dōng shān jiǔ

蔷薇几度花②。
qiáng wēi jǐ dù huā

白云还自散，
bái yún hái zì sàn

明月落谁家③？
míng yuè luò shéi jiā

注释

① 东山：在会稽上虞（今属浙江）西南，是东晋著名宰相谢安早年的隐居之处。后代多以此代指隐居、归隐。

② "蔷薇"句：东山附近有蔷薇洞，相传是谢安的游宴之地。

③ "白云"二句：以白云、明月的无主喻指隐者不归，同时寄寓着自己的归隐之志趣。白云、明月既是实指物象，又暗指谢安在东山所建的白云、明月二堂。

第五单元

chén dú duì yùn jiǔ
晨 读 对 韵（九）

qí
齐（i）

hé duì hǎi jiàn duì xī yuǎn jìn duì gāo dī
河对海，涧对溪，远近对高低。

qí zhēn duì yì bǎo hǔ pò duì liú li
奇珍对异宝，琥珀对琉璃。

táo zhuó zhuó liǔ yī yī
桃灼灼，柳依依。

lóng yǎn duì mǎ tí
龙眼对马蹄①。

jū shuǐ yuè zài shǒu niān huā xiāng mǎn yī
掬水月在手，拈花香满衣。

jǐ chù zǎo yīng zhēng nuǎn shù
几处早莺争暖树，

shéi jiā xīn yàn zhuó chūn ní
谁家新燕啄春泥。

① 龙眼：桂圆的俗称。马蹄：荸荠的俗称。

晨读对韵（十）

齐（i）

来对往，密对稀，来日对往昔。

眼明对手快，心旷对神怡。

千里马，五更鸡。

暮霭对晨曦。

高谈惊左右，博学贯中西。

天上月悬千古镜，

池中星照一盘棋。

开满鲜花的头

[意大利] 贾尼·罗大里

如果头上不长头发，

种满鲜花该是怎样的景象？

一眼就可看出，

谁心地善良，谁心情悲伤。

前额长着一束玫瑰花的人，

不会做坏事。

头上长着沉默的紫罗兰的人，

有点儿黑色幽默。

顶着一头零乱的大荨麻的人呢？

yí dìng sī wéi hùn luàn
一 定 思 维 混 乱，

měi tiān zǎo chen tú láo de
每 天 早 晨 徒 劳 地

làng fèi yì píng huò liǎng píng tóu yóu
浪 费 一 瓶 或 两 瓶 头 油。

xíng wén jiàn qí hàn yì
（邢 文 健，亓 菡 译）

以一个新奇的想法开头，会引出多少稀奇古怪的联想。精巧的构思，把我们带入了一个神奇的幻想世界。让我们也来一起想一想，如果头上不长头发，会长成什么样？

lǎo tóu dēng
老头灯

◎ mín jiān tóng yáo
民间童谣

lǎo tóu dēng　　lǎo mā dēng
老头灯，老妈灯，

lái le sān gè kàn dēng rén
来了三个看灯人。

lóng zi tā shuō pào bù xiǎng
聋子他说炮不响；

xiā zi tā shuō dēng bù míng
瞎子他说灯不明。

bǒ zi tīng le nù chōng chōng
跛子听了怒冲冲：

nǐ men liǎng gè jiáo shé gēn
你们两个嚼舌根；

pào yě xiǎng　　dēng yě míng
炮也响，灯也明。

zhǐ guài shì shàng lù bù píng
只怪世上路不平。

赏析

　　这是一首充满幽默的童谣。三个看灯人因为自身的不足对灯展妄加批评，读来令人捧腹。

shān zhōng sòng bié
山 中 送 别

táng wáng wéi
（唐）王 维

shān zhōng xiāng sòng bà
山 中 相 送 罢，

rì mù yǎn chái fēi
日 暮 掩 柴 扉 ①。

chūn cǎo míng nián lǜ
春 草 明 年 绿，

wáng sūn guī bù guī
王 孙 归 不 归？

注释 ① 日暮：黄昏时分。柴扉：柴门。

第六单元

chén dú duì yùn shí yī
晨 读 对 韵（十 一）

wēi
微（ei ui）

kuān duì zhǎi xiǎn duì wēi shǎn diàn duì míng léi
宽 对 窄，显 对 微，闪 电 对 鸣 雷。

tiān nán duì hǎi běi hóng shòu duì lǜ féi
天 南 对 海 北，红 瘦 对 绿 肥①。

cháo zhǎng luò yuè yíng kuī
潮 涨 落，月 盈 亏。

mù sè duì zhāo huī
暮 色 对 朝 晖。

míng yuè sōng jiān zhào chūn fēng liǔ shàng guī
明 月 松 间 照，春 风 柳 上 归。

chuān huā jiá dié shēn shēn xiàn
穿 花 蛱 蝶 深 深 见②，

diǎn shuǐ qīng tíng kuǎn kuǎn fēi
点 水 蜻 蜓 款 款 飞。

 注释

① 红瘦：红花稀少。绿肥：枝叶繁茂。
② 蛱蝶：蝴蝶的一类。

chén dú duì yùn shí èr
晨 读 对 韵（十 二）

wēi
微（ei ui）

piān duì zhèng shì duì fēi xīn xǐ duì shāng bēi
偏 对 正，是 对 非，欣 喜 对 伤 悲。

qīng shān duì lǜ shuǐ cǎo shè duì chái fēi
青 山 对 绿 水，草 舍 对 柴 扉。

shān tū wù shuǐ yíng huí
山 突 兀，水 潆 洄①。

yǔ dǎ duì fēng chuī
雨 打 对 风 吹。

tiān dì rù xiōng yì wén zhāng shēng fēng léi
天 地 入 胸 臆，文 章 生 风 雷。

ào gǔ xū xīn zhēn lì liàng
傲 骨 虚 心 真 力 量，

rè cháng lěng yǎn dà cí bēi
热 肠 冷 眼 大 慈 悲②。

① 潆洄：形容水流回旋。
② 为《大公报》及辅仁大学创始人英敛之先生座右铭。

127

guò nián
过 年

（中国台湾）洪志明
zhōng guó tái wān hóng zhì míng

kě wù de biān pào
可恶的鞭炮

chǎo xǐng le wǒ
吵醒了我

hái yào qù chǎo xǐng dì di
还要去吵醒弟弟

chǎo xǐng le wǒ
吵醒了我

méi guān xi
没关系

wǒ hái kě yǐ zài shuì
我还可以再睡

chǎo xǐng le dì di
吵醒了弟弟

jiù bù dé liǎo
就不得了

dì di de kū shēng shì yí chuàn
弟弟的哭声是一串

fàng bù wán de biān pào
放不完的鞭炮

chǎo de quán jiā rén
吵得全家人

dōu méi bàn fǎ shuì jiào
都没办法睡觉

赏析　　过年时放鞭炮，本来是一件快乐的事情。可作者却反其道而行，批评鞭炮太可恶。最后一句通过迁移的方式，说出了家中有个爱哭的小弟弟的烦恼，读来觉得形象、可爱。

gāo gāo shān shang yì kē má
高 高 山 上 一 棵 麻

mín jiān tóng yáo
◎ 民 间 童 谣

gāo gāo shān shang yì kē má
高高山 上 一 棵 麻，

liǎng gè qū qu er wǎng shàng pá
两个蛐蛐儿 往 上 爬。

yí gè qū qu er ài hē jiǔ
一个蛐蛐儿 爱 喝 酒。

yí gè qū qu er ài hē chá
一个蛐蛐儿 爱 喝 茶。

jiǔ yě hē bù liǎo
酒也喝不了，

chá yě hē bù liǎo
茶也喝不了，

zhī qǐ gǔ lái chàng shān gē
支起鼓来 唱 山 歌，

chàng de hǎo lái bié shuō hǎo
唱 得好来别 说 好，

chàng de bù hǎo bié dǎ wǒ
唱 得不好别 打 我。

láo láo tíng
劳 劳 亭 ①

táng lǐ bái
（唐）李 白

tiān xià shāng xīn chù
天 下 伤 心 处，

láo láo sòng kè tíng
劳 劳 送 客 亭。

chūn fēng zhī bié kǔ
春 风 知 别 苦②，

bù qiǎn liǔ tiáo qīng
不 遣 柳 条 青③。

① 劳劳亭：原名望远楼，故址在现在南京市南。
② "春风"句：春风知道离别的苦楚。
③ 遣：令，让。

这是一首伤感的送别诗。古有折柳送别的习俗，而春风显得善解人意，柳条未青，让离人无柳可折。但在劳劳亭处，依旧是别情依依，让人更添惆怅。

第七单元

chén dú duì yùn   shí sān
晨 读 对 韵（十 三）

kāi
开（ai）

zhāo duì mù shèng duì shuāi wǔ xiè duì gē tái
朝 对 暮，盛 对 衰，舞 榭 对 歌 台。

fēng qīng duì yuè lǎng xì yuàn duì shū zhāi
风 清 对 月 朗，戏 院 对 书 斋。

táo yè dù   yǔ huā tái
桃 叶 渡 ①，雨 花 台 ②。

qíng rì duì yīn mái
晴 日 对 阴 霾。

bì táo hé lù zhòng hóng xìng yǐ yún zāi
碧 桃 和 露 种，红 杏 倚 云 栽。

tiān wài hēi fēng chuī hǎi lì
天 外 黑 风 吹 海 立，

zhè dōng fēi yǔ guò jiāng lái
浙 东 飞 雨 过 江 来。

注释

① 桃叶渡：地名，在今南京市内秦淮河、青溪合流处。
② 雨花台：地名，在今南京市中华门外。

chén dú duì yùn shí sì
晨 读 对 韵（十 四）

kāi
开（ai）

yōu duì xǐ lè duì āi xìn rèn duì yí cāi
忧 对 喜，乐 对 哀，信 任 对 疑 猜。

fēng cān duì lù sù bù shǔ duì ān pái
风 餐 对 露 宿，部 署 对 安 排。

shī qiǎn xìng jiǔ kāi huái
诗 遣 兴，酒 开 怀。

hóng yè duì lǜ tái
红 叶 对 绿 苔。

jiāng cóng wàn lǐ zhì shān zuò liǎng méi kāi
江 从 万 里 至，山 作 两 眉 开。

bō hún wèi biàn yú lóng jì
波 浑 未 辨 鱼 龙 迹，

suì hán fāng shí dòng liáng cái
岁 寒 方 识 栋 梁 材。

为天量身高

（中国台湾）子鱼

什么

没有人知道

天到底有多高

这让大地感到不可思议

决定请小孩子帮忙丈量丈量

天到底有多高

小孩子放起风筝

lǎ
拉

cháng
长

xiàn
线

wèi
为

tiān
天

liáng
量

shēn
身

gāo
高

zhàn hǎo bié luàn dòng o fēng zheng shuō
"站 好,别 乱 动 哦!"风 筝 说

tiān
天

méi dòng
没 动

赏析　　让风筝为天空量身高,多么大胆的想法!又是多么绝妙的主意!特别是诗中"拉长线为天量身高"这几个字,一个一个斜着排列,真像风筝那长长的线,多么巧妙呀!

zhāi yīng tao
摘 樱 桃

xú huàn yún
◎ 徐 焕 云

yīng tao shù
樱 桃 树，

wān wān yāo
弯 弯 腰，

yīng tao shú le
樱 桃 熟 了，

yáo yáo yáo
摇 摇 摇。

yé ye zhāi
爷 爷 摘，

sūn er zhāi
孙 儿 摘，

liú xià jǐ kē
留 下 几 颗，

wèi xiǎo niǎo
喂 小 鸟。

zhú   lǐ   guǎn
竹 里 馆 ①

táng   wáng wéi
（唐 ）王 维

dú zuò yōu huáng lǐ
独 坐 幽 篁 里 ②，

tán qín fù cháng xiào
弹 琴 复 长 啸 ③。

shēn lín rén bù zhī
深 林 人 不 知，

míng yuè lái xiāng zhào
明 月 来 相 照。

① 竹里馆：王维诗集《辋川集》的第十七首。
② 幽篁：幽静的竹林。篁，竹林。
③ 啸：撮口发出长而清脆的声音。

　　这是诗人晚年隐居生活的生动写照。用简朴清丽的语言描写了诗人山林幽居生活的环境和清静安详的心境。

晨 读 对 韵（十 五）

chén dú duì yùn shí wǔ

模（u）

mú

秦 对 晋，越 对 吴，南 海 对 西 湖。

qín duì jìn，yuè duì wú，nán hǎi duì xī hú

鸢 飞 对 鱼 跃，鹦 鹉 对 鹧 鸪。

yuān fēi duì yú yuè，yīng wǔ duì zhè gū

青 玉 案，紫 砂 壶。

qīng yù àn，zǐ shā hú

李 白 对 杨 朱①。

lǐ bái duì yáng zhū

儿 童 骑 竹 马②，旅 客 忆 莼 鲈③。

ér tóng qí zhú mǎ，lǚ kè yì chún lú

落 叶 舞 风 高 复 下，小 荷 浮 水 卷 还 舒。

luò yè wǔ fēng gāo fù xià，xiǎo hé fú shuǐ juǎn hái shū

注释

① 杨朱：战国时思想家。
② 竹马：古代儿童游戏时当马骑的竹竿。
③ 莼鲈：莼菜和鲈鱼，产于江浙，味道鲜美。

chén dú duì yùn shí liù
晨 读 对 韵（十 六）

mú
模（u）

shēng duì sǐ xiào duì kū měi yù duì míng zhū
生 对 死，笑 对 哭，美 玉 对 明 珠。

rén qíng duì shì gù kùn jìng duì tōng tú
人 情 对 世 故，困 境 对 通 途。

sān dū fù   bā zhèn tú
三 都 赋 ①，八 阵 图 ②。

guǒ duàn duì chóu chú
果 断 对 踌 躇 ③。

yān qīng lǒng àn liǔ fēng jí hàn tíng wú
烟 轻 笼 岸 柳，风 急 撼 庭 梧。

zhuàng shì yāo jiān sān chǐ jiàn nán ér fù nèi wǔ chē shū
壮 士 腰 间 三 尺 剑，男 儿 腹 内 五 车 书。

① 三都赋：西晋诗人左思以十年心血创作的名篇，当时文人学士们争相抄阅，造成"洛阳纸贵"。

② 八阵图：古代作战时的一种战斗队形及兵力部署，据传是诸葛亮发明的。

③ 踌躇：犹豫不决。

shén me jiān jiān jiān shàng tiān
什 么 尖 尖 尖 上 天

mín jiān tóng yáo
◎ 民 间 童 谣

shén me jiān jiān jiān shàng tiān
什 么 尖 尖 尖 上 天？

shén me jiān jiān zài shuǐ biān
什 么 尖 尖 在 水 边？

shén me jiān jiān jiē shang mài
什 么 尖 尖 街 上 卖？

shén me jiān jiān gū niang qián
什 么 尖 尖 姑 娘 前？

bǎo tǎ jiān jiān jiān shàng tiān
宝 塔 尖 尖 尖 上 天，

líng jiao jiān jiān zài shuǐ biān
菱 角 尖 尖 在 水 边，

zòng zi jiān jiān jiē shang mài
粽 子 尖 尖 街 上 卖，

huā zhēn er jiān jiān gū niang qián
花 针 儿 尖 尖 姑 娘 前。

shén me yuán yuán yuán shàng tiān
什 么 圆 圆 圆 上 天？

shén me yuán yuán zài shuǐ biān
什么圆圆在水边？

shén me yuán yuán jiē shang mài
什么圆圆街上卖？

shén me yuán yuán gū niang qián
什么圆圆姑娘前？

tài yáng yuán yuán yuán shàng tiān
太阳圆圆圆上天，

hé yè yuán yuán zài shuǐ biān
荷叶圆圆在水边，

shāo bing yuán yuán jiē shang mài
烧饼圆圆街上卖，

jìng zi yuán yuán gū niang qián
镜子圆圆姑娘前。

shén me fāng fāng fāng shàng tiān
什么方方方上天？

shén me fāng fāng zài shuǐ biān
什么方方在水边？

shén me fāng fāng jiē shang mài
什么方方街上卖？

shén me fāng fāng gū niang qián
什么方方姑娘前？

fēng zheng fāng fāng fāng shàng tiān
风筝方方方上天，

sī wǎng fāng fāng zài shuǐ biān
丝网方方在水边，

dòu fu fāng fāng jiē shang mài
豆腐方方街上卖，

shǒu jīn fāng fāng gū niang qián
手巾方方姑娘前。

shén me wān wān wān shàng tiān
什么弯弯弯上天？

shén me wān wān zài shuǐ biān
什么弯弯在水边？

shén me wān wān jiē shang mài
什么弯弯街上卖？

shén me wān wān gū niang qián
什么弯弯姑娘前？

yuè liang wān wān wān shàng tiān
月亮弯弯弯上天，

bái ǒu wān wān zài shuǐ biān
白藕弯弯在水边，

huáng guā wān wān jiē shang mài
黄瓜弯弯街上卖，

mù shū wān wān gū niang qián
木梳弯弯姑娘前。

wǒ shì cǎo méi
我 是 草 莓

měi guó kù sī jīn
〔美 国〕库 斯 金

wǒ xǐ huan shēng zhǎng
我 喜 欢 生 长，

shēng zhǎng zhēn jiào rén xǐ huan
生 长 真 叫 人 喜 欢。

yè zi ruǎn ruǎn de
叶 子 软 软 的，

tài yáng nuǎn nuǎn de
太 阳 暖 暖 的。

wǒ shú le hóng le yuán le
我 熟 了 红 了 圆 了，

jiù yǒu rén bǎ wǒ rēng dào le
就 有 人 把 我 扔 到 了

lǒu zi lǐ bian
篓 子 里 边。

zuò cǎo méi bú shì zǒng
做 草 莓 不 是 总

nà me hǎo wán
那 么 好 玩。

jīn tiān zǎo chen tā men
今 天 早 晨 他 们

bǎ wǒ fàng jìn bīng jī líng
把 我 放 进 冰 激 凌，

wǒ lěng de zhí dǎ zhàn zhan
我 冷 得 直 打 战 战。

wáng shì yuè yì
（王 世 跃 译）

赏析　　这首小诗的作者把自己想象成草莓，体验了一下草莓的感受。既有温暖又有寒气，让孩子领悟到：即使是一颗小小的草莓，生活也并非总是那么好玩，活泼有趣而又意味深长。

142

lù   zhài

鹿 柴 ①

táng wáng wéi
（唐）王 维

kōng shān bú jiàn rén
空 山 不 见 人 ②，

dàn wén rén yǔ xiǎng
但 闻 人 语 响 ③。

fǎn yǐng rù shēn lín
返 景 入 深 林 ④，

fù zhào qīng tái shàng
复 照 青 苔 上 。

① 鹿柴：鹿栖止的地方，是辋川别墅的一个景点。
② 空山：寂静无人的山。
③ 但闻：只听见。人语响：人说话的声音。
④ 返景：夕阳的返照。景，同"影"，日光。

这是一首极富画面感的诗。前两句写声，以"人语响"反衬空谷的静寂；后两句写景，突出描绘了鹿柴的幽静与美妙。

第九单元

chén dú duì yùn shí qī
晨 读 对 韵(十 七)

yú
鱼(ü)

zhōng duì shǐ gōng duì xū rǎn rǎn duì xú xú
终 对 始,供 对 需,冉 冉 对 徐 徐。

qīng tiān duì bì hǎi xiǎo dào duì tōng qú
青 天 对 碧 海,小 道 对 通 衢①。

hóng sháo yao bái fú qú
红 芍 药,白 芙 蕖②。

qǐ zǐ duì sāng yú
杞 梓 对 桑 榆③。

fú yún lián hǎi dài píng yě rù qīng xú
浮 云 连 海 岱,平 野 入 青 徐。

táo huā hóng yā bō li shuǐ
桃 花 红 压 玻 璃 水,

píng zǎo shēn cáng fěi cuì yú
萍 藻 深 藏 翡 翠 鱼④。

注释

① 通衢:四通八达的大道。
② 芙蕖:莲花。
③ 杞梓:两种优质的木材,比喻优秀人才。桑榆:桑树和榆树,比喻人的晚年。
④ 浙江杭州西湖玉泉楹联。

晨 读 对 韵（十 八）
chén dú duì yùn shí bā

鱼（ü）
yú

rén duì jǐ zhì duì yú dì shì duì shí jú
人 对 己，智 对 愚，地 势 对 时 局。

huān shēng duì xiào yǔ cháng jiǔ duì xū yú
欢 声 对 笑 语，长 久 对 须 臾。

yīng bǔ tù lù kuī yú
鹰 捕 兔，鹭 窥 鱼。

bìng jià duì qí qū
并 驾 对 齐 驱。

lǚ xiǎn xīn yóu jìng lín wēi zhì bù yú
履 险 心 犹 静，临 危 志 不 渝。

dàn qiú wén zì chuán qīng jiǎn
但 求 文 字 传 青 简①，

yuàn jiè fú yáo shàng bì xū
愿 借 扶 摇 上 碧 虚②。

① 青简：古代书籍用狭长的竹片编成，故称书籍为"青简"。
② 碧虚：天空。

145

jiù wǒ yí gè rén de shí hou
就 我 一 个 人 的 时 候

měi guó　ài　gé lín fēi ěr
[美 国] 爱·格林菲尔

jiù wǒ yí gè rén de shí hou
就 我 一 个 人 的 时 候，

bì qǐ yǎn jing wǒ zhēn kuài huo
闭 起 眼 睛，我 真 快 活。

wǒ shì shuāng bāo tāi
我 是 双 胞 胎，

wǒ shì xiǎo jiǔ wō er
我 是 小 酒 窝 儿，

wǒ shì wán jù cāng kù
我 是 玩 具 仓 库，

wǒ shì dòng rén de gē er
我 是 动 人 的 歌 儿，

wǒ shì zī zī jiào de sōng shǔ
我 是 吱 吱 叫 的 松 鼠，

wǒ shì yí miàn tóng luó
我 是 一 面 铜 锣，

wǒ shì zōng sè de miàn bāo pí
我 是 棕 色 的 面 包 皮，

wǒ shì shù zhī biàn chéng le hóng sè
我 是 树 枝 变 成 了 红 色……

fǎn zhèng
反 正,

wǒ xiǎng shì shén me jiù shì shén me
我 想 是 什 么,就 是 什 么,

wǒ yuàn zuò shén me jiù néng zuò shén me
我 愿 做 什 么,就 能 做 什 么。

kě shì yì zhēng kāi yǎn jing
可 是,一 睁 开 眼 睛,

āi
唉!

wǒ hái shì wǒ
我 还 是 我。

wáng jì mín yì
(王 济 民 译)

赏析

　　孩子的想象是无限的,一个人的时候一闭上眼睛,许多想法就会吱吱地长了出来。这种直抒胸臆的表达方式让人感觉非常亲切。

shān gē bú chàng wàng jì duō
山　歌　不　唱　忘　记　多

shān gē bú chàng wàng jì duō
山　歌　不　唱　忘　记　多，

dà lù bù zǒu cǎo chéng kē
大　路　不　走　草　成　窠；

kuài dāo bù mó huáng xiù qǐ
快　刀　不　磨　黄　锈　起，

xiōng táng bù tǐng bèi yào tuó
胸　膛　不　挺　背　要　驼。

　　这首儿歌每行七字，句式整齐，例举了常见的生活经验，告诉我们一个浅显的道理：凡事需多多练习。和孩子一起诵读，也可以让他们接下去说说。

148

江南曲四首（其三）

（唐）储光羲

日暮长江里，

相邀归渡头①。

落花如有意，

来去逐轻舟②。

① 渡头：渡口。

② 逐：追逐，追随。

第十单元

chén dú duì yùn　shí jiǔ
晨读对韵（十九）

hóu
侯(ou iu)

māo duì gǒu què duì jiū hé mǎ duì shuǐ niú
猫 对 狗,鹊 对 鸠,河 马 对 水 牛。

jiāng fēng duì hǎi wù shèng xià duì qīng qiū
江 风 对 海 雾,盛 夏 对 清 秋。

fēng yǎ sòng　　xià shāng zhōu
风 雅 颂①,夏 商 周②。

qīng niǎo duì bái ōu
青 鸟 对 白 鸥。

dà mò shā rú xuě yān shān yuè sì gōu
大 漠 沙 如 雪,燕 山 月 似 钩。

rì wǎn ài xíng shēn zhú lǐ
日 晚 爱 行 深 竹 里,

yuè míng duō shàng xiǎo qiáo tóu
月 明 多 上 小 桥 头。

注释

① 风雅颂:我国最早的诗歌总集《诗经》,根据作品乐调的不同,将其分为风、雅、颂三部分。

② 夏商周:我国历史上最早的三个朝代。

chén dú duì yùn   èr shí
晨 读 对 韵（二 十）

hóu
侯（ou iu）

róng duì rǔ xǐ duì yōu hào chǐ duì míng móu
荣 对 辱，喜 对 忧，皓 齿 对 明 眸。

tiān wén duì dì lǐ yù yǔ duì qióng lóu
天 文 对 地 理，玉 宇 对 琼 楼。

shān jì jì shuǐ yōu yōu
山 寂 寂，水 悠 悠。

sì hǎi duì jiǔ zhōu
四 海 对 九 州。

yù qióng qiān lǐ mù gèng shàng yì céng lóu
欲 穷 千 里 目，更 上 一 层 楼。

shū shān yǒu lù qín wéi jìng
书 山 有 路 勤 为 径，

xué hǎi wú yá kǔ zuò zhōu
学 海 无 涯 苦 作 舟①。

注释　　① 此联流传甚广，商友敬老师改为"书山有路思为径，学海无涯趣作舟"。虽改两字，但意味深长。

151

小猫晒太阳
xiǎo māo shài tài yáng

zhōng guó tái wān　lín huàn zhāng
（中 国 台 湾）林 焕 彰

xiǎo māo zài yáng tái shang
小 猫 在 阳 台 上

shài tài yang
晒 太 阳，

tā xǐ huān bǎ zì jǐ juǎn chéng yí gè
它 喜 欢 把 自 己 卷 成 一 个

xiǎo xiǎo de máo xiàn qiú
小 小 的 毛 线 球，

shōu jí dōng tiān de yáng guāng
收 集 冬 天 的 阳 光。

赏析　　冬天里，最舒服的事情就是晒太阳了，坐在阳光下面，寒冷一点点被赶走，温暖一点点把我们包围。让我们来看看晒太阳的小猫：哈！变成了一个小小的毛线球，在阳光下，金灿灿，毛绒绒，好舒服，好温暖！多么可爱的小猫，多么温暖的小诗啊！

chūn tiān bèi mài guāng le
春 天 被 卖 光 了

zhōng guó tái wān   dù róng chēn
（中 国 台 湾）杜 荣 琛

chūn tiān shì yì pǐ
春 天 是 一 匹

shì jiè shang zuì měi lì de cǎi bù
世 界 上 最 美 丽 的 彩 布，

yàn zi shì gè mài bù láng
燕 子 是 个 卖 布 郎。

tā suí shēn dài zhe yì bǎ jiǎn dāo
他 随 身 带 着 一 把 剪 刀，

měi tiān máng lù de dōng fēi fei
每 天 忙 碌 地 东 飞 飞，

xī jiǎn jian
西 剪 剪，

bǎ chūn tiān yí cùn cùn mài guāng le
把 春 天 一 寸 寸 卖 光 了。

赏析

燕子是个卖布郎，把春天一寸一寸卖光了。多形象的比喻，多新奇的构思，写出了春天的忙碌，也写出了春光的易逝。

jué jù
绝 句

táng dù fǔ
（唐）杜 甫

jiāng bì niǎo yú bái
江 碧 鸟 逾 白 ①，

shān qīng huā yù rán
山 青 花 欲 燃。

jīn chūn kàn yòu guò
今 春 看 又 过，

hé rì shì guī nián
何 日 是 归 年？

① 逾：更加。

第十一单元

chén dú duì yùn èr shí yī
晨 读 对 韵（二 十 一）

háo
豪（ao）

méi duì xìng lǐ duì táo sháo yao duì bā jiāo
梅对杏,李对桃,芍药对芭蕉。

chūn fēn duì xià zhì shuǐ yuǎn duì shān yáo
春分对夏至,水远对山遥。

fēng sà sà yǔ xiāo xiāo
风飒飒,雨潇潇。

mài suì duì hé miáo
麦穗对禾苗。

qīng yú qián lǜ shuǐ bái hè shàng bì xiāo
青鱼潜绿水,白鹤上碧霄。

yān huǒ wàn jiā rén liǎng àn
烟火万家人两岸,

chūn jiāng yì qǔ liǔ qiān tiáo
春江一曲柳千条。

chén dú duì yùn èr shí èr
晨 读 对 韵（二 十 二）

háo
豪（ɑo）

nán duì yì biǎn duì bāo yǒu qù duì wú liáo
难 对 易，贬 对 褒，有 趣 对 无 聊。

léi shēng duì diàn yǐng huǒ jiàn duì xuě qiāo
雷 声 对 电 影，火 箭 对 雪 橇。

jiāo yì wǔ jiàn shēn cāo wǔ jiàn duì huī dāo
交 谊 舞，健 身 操，舞 剑 对 挥 刀。

lóu guān cāng hǎi rì mén duì zhè jiāng cháo
楼 观 沧 海 日，门 对 浙 江 潮。

yīng xióng zì gǔ pī gān dǎn
英 雄 自 古 披 肝 胆，

zhì shì hé cháng xī yǔ máo
志 士 何 尝 惜 羽 毛①。

① 选自清代李秀成《感事诗》。

156

jú huā kāi
菊花开

◎ 佚名

板凳，板凳，歪歪，

菊花，菊花，开开！

开几朵？

开三朵；

爹一朵，娘一朵，

剩下那朵给白鸽。

前两行句式相同，两字一顿，节奏感强。后四行一问一答，表达了孩子对父母、对自然的喜爱之情。

眼　泪

[捷克斯洛伐克]格鲁宾

谁想哭鼻子谁哭去吧，

我倒不哭。那玩意儿我不喜欢。

我还为爱哭鼻子的小朋友可惜哩：

因为漾着泪水的眼看不见太阳！

（韦苇　译）

赏析　　诗人用俏皮的语言讲述了一个深刻的主题：乐观向上，才能看见生活中的阳光。短短四行，言简意赅而又令人回味无穷。

bā zhèn tú
八 阵 图 ①

táng dù fǔ
（唐）杜 甫

gōng gài sān fēn guó
功 盖 三 分 国 ②，

míng chéng bā zhèn tú
名 成 八 阵 图。

jiāng liú shí bù zhuǎn
江 流 石 不 转 ③，

yí hèn shī tūn wú
遗 恨 失 吞 吴 ④。

① 八阵图：诸葛亮为抵御吴兵而在长江边沙滩上设置的一种战阵。

② 盖：在最上边。这里意思是超过其他。三分国：指分立天下的魏、蜀、吴三国。

③ 石不转：指涨水时，八阵图的石块仍然不动。

④ 失吞吴：是吞吴失策的意思。

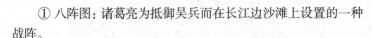

第十二单元

chén dú duì yùn   èr shí sān
晨 读 对 韵（二 十 三）

hán
寒（an）

qiān duì bǎi liǎng duì sān sài běi duì jiāng nán
千 对 百，两 对 三，塞 北 对 江 南。

shān cūn duì hǎi dǎo kuàng yě duì píng yuán
山 村 对 海 岛，旷 野 对 平 原。

huā làn màn   yuè chán juān
花 烂 漫 ①，月 婵 娟 ②。

cǎo mù duì shān chuān
草 木 对 山 川。

yīng huā hóng mò shàng liǔ yè lǜ chí biān
樱 花 红 陌 上，柳 叶 绿 池 边。

sān chūn bái xuě guī qīng zhǒng
三 春 白 雪 归 青 冢 ③，

wàn lǐ huáng hé rào hēi shān
万 里 黄 河 绕 黑 山。

注
释

① 烂漫：颜色鲜艳的样子。

② 婵娟：美好的样子。

③ 青冢：王昭君墓，在呼和浩特大黑河南岸的冲积平原上，墓上芳草萋萋，故称"青冢"。

chén dú duì yùn（èr shí sì）
晨 读 对 韵（二 十 四）

hán
寒（an）

zhōng duì wài shèng duì xián jǔ zhǐ duì guān zhān
中 对 外，圣 对 贤，举 止 对 观 瞻。

zhī fán duì yè mào guī ju duì fāng yuán
枝 繁 对 叶 茂，规 矩 对 方 圆。

shuǐ yuè sì shān hǎi guān
水 月 寺，山 海 关 ①。

yǔ mù duì yún yān
雨 幕 对 云 烟。

yuè lái mǎn dì shuǐ yún qǐ yì tiān shān
月 来 满 地 水，云 起 一 天 山 ②。

shào nián shuō jiàn qì héng dǒu
少 年 说 剑 气 横 斗，

cháng yè dú shū shēng mǎn tiān
长 夜 读 书 声 满 天。

① 清咸丰年间，彭俊中状元，与友畅游北京水月寺，老僧知其为状元，出上联"水月寺，鱼游兔走"，彭俊一时难住，无法对出。后来他因事路过山海关，猛然间想出下联"山海关，虎啸龙吟"。

② 扬州瘦西湖月观亭楹联，相传是郑板桥所作。

zǒng děi yǒu rén qù cā xīng xing
总 得 有 人 去 擦 星 星

měi guó xiè ěr xī ěr fú sī tǎn
[美国] 谢尔·希尔弗斯坦

zǒng děi yǒu rén qù cā xīng xing
总 得 有 人 去 擦 星 星，

tā men kàn qi lai huī méng méng
它 们 看 起 来 灰 蒙 蒙。

zǒng děi yǒu rén qù cā xīng xing
总 得 有 人 去 擦 星 星，

yīn wèi nà xiē bā ge hǎi ōu hé lǎo yīng
因 为 那 些 八 哥、海 鸥 和 老 鹰

dōu bào yuàn xīng xing yòu jiù yòu shēng xiù
都 抱 怨 星 星 又 旧 又 生 锈，

xiǎng yào gè xīn de wǒ men méi yǒu
想 要 个 新 的 我 们 没 有。

suǒ yǐ hái shì dài shàng shuǐ tǒng hé mā bù
所 以 还 是 带 上 水 桶 和 抹 布，

zǒng děi yǒu rén qù cā xīng xing
总 得 有 人 去 擦 星 星。

yè shuò yì
（叶 硕 译）

　　天空中的星星看起来灰蒙蒙的,怎么办呢？想换新的我们又没有,那就只好带上水桶和抹布,去把星星擦亮。小诗从孩子的心理出发,表现了孩子满怀善意的天真想法。

dà qīng tíng
大　蜻　蜓

◎ yì míng
◎ 佚　名

dà qīng tíng
大 蜻 蜓,

lǜ yǎn jing
绿 眼 睛,

liǎng duì chì bǎng liàng jīng jīng
两 对 翅 膀 亮 晶 晶。

fēi yì fēi
飞 一 飞,

tíng yì tíng
停 一 停,

fēi lái fēi qù zhuō wén yíng
飞 来 飞 去 捉 蚊 蝇。

赏析

　　蜻蜓是小朋友非常喜爱的小精灵。这首儿歌用三七句式介绍了蜻蜓的外形与生活习性,读来清新明快,令人愉悦。

táo zhě
陶　　者

sòng　méi yáo chén
（宋）梅尧臣

táo　jìn　mén qián　tǔ
陶　尽　门　前　土①，

wū shàng wú piàn wǎ
屋　上　无　片　瓦。

shí　zhǐ　bù　zhān　ní
十　指　不　沾　泥，

lín　lín　jū　dà　shà
鳞　鳞　居　大　厦②。

① 陶：作动词，烧陶。这里指烧瓦。
② 鳞鳞：形容屋上的瓦片重叠，一片片像鱼鳞一样。

第十三单元

chén dú duì yùn   èr shí wǔ
晨 读 对 韵（二 十 五）

hén
痕（en un in ün）

hán duì shǔ yè duì chén bái zhòu duì huáng hūn
寒 对 暑，夜 对 晨，白 昼 对 黄 昏。

shān míng duì shuǐ xiù hǔ xiào duì lóng yín
山 明 对 水 秀，虎 啸 对 龙 吟。

cāng hǎi yuè bì tiān yún shā mò duì sēn lín
沧 海 月，碧 天 云，沙 漠 对 森 林。

hóng rù táo huā nèn qīng guī liǔ yè xīn
红 入 桃 花 嫩，青 归 柳 叶 新。

chén zhōu cè pàn qiān fān guò
沉 舟 侧 畔 千 帆 过，

bìng shù qián tóu wàn mù chūn
病 树 前 头 万 木 春。

chén dú duì yùn èr shí liù
晨 读 对 韵（二 十 六）

hén
痕（en un in ün）

méi duì mù kǒu duì xīn jǐn sè duì yáo qín
眉 对 目，口 对 心，锦 瑟 对 瑶 琴。

liú guāng duì shì shuǐ zhuàng zhì duì xióng xīn
流 光 对 逝 水，壮 志 对 雄 心。

wǔ cǎi lù qī xián qín
五 彩 路，七 弦 琴。

liáo luàn duì fēn yún
缭 乱 对 纷 纭。

bǐ luò jīng fēng yǔ shī chéng qì guǐ shén
笔 落 惊 风 雨，诗 成 泣 鬼 神。

bái yún bái niǎo fēi lái qù
白 云 白 鸟 飞 来 去，

qīng shǐ qīng shān zì gǔ jīn
青 史 青 山 自 古 今①。

注释　　① 香港青山禅院海月亭楹联。

bā zhā   bā zhā
巴 喳——巴 喳

yīng guó jié lǐ fú cí
[英 国]杰·里弗茨

chuān shàng dà pí xuē zài lín zi li zǒu
穿 上 大 皮 靴 在 林 子 里 走,

bā zhā   bā zhā
巴 喳——巴 喳!

dǔ dǔ tīng jiàn zhè shēng yīn
"笃笃"听见这声音,

jiù yí xià duǒ dào le shù zhī jiān
就一下躲到了树枝间。

zī zī yí xià cuàn shàng le sōng shù
"吱吱"一下窜上了松树,

bèng bèng yí xià zuān jìn le mì lín
"蹦蹦"一下钻进了密林。

jī jī dū yí xià fēi jìn lǜ yè zhōng
"叽叽"嘟一下飞进绿叶中,

shā shā chī yí xià liū jìn le hēi dòng
"沙沙"哧一下溜进了黑洞。

quán dōu qiǎo mo shēng er de dūn zài
全 都 悄 没 声 儿 地 蹲 在

kàn bú jiàn de dì fang
看 不 见 的 地 方，

mù bù zhuǎn jīng de kàn zhe
目 不 转 睛 地 看 着

bā zhā   bā zhā
"巴 喳——巴 喳"

yuè zǒu yuè yuǎn
越 走 越 远。

wéi wéi   yì
（韦 苇 译）

原来声音也会做游戏呀！请大家一起来猜猜"巴喳——巴喳!""笃笃""吱吱""蹦蹦""叽叽""沙沙"都是谁的声音，还可以一起来演一演这首小诗，一定非常有趣。

gāo gāo shān shang yì tóu niú
高 高 山 上 一 头 牛

mín jiān tóng yáo
◎ 民 间 童 谣

gāo gāo shān shang yì tóu niú
高 高 山 上 一 头 牛，

liǎng gè jī jiao yí gè tóu
两 个 犄 角 一 个 头；

sì gè tí zi fēn bā bàn
四 个 蹄 子 分 八 瓣，

wěi ba zhǎng zài shēn hòu tou
尾 巴 长 在 身 后 头。

kè xiǎo
客 晓

（清）沈受宏
qīng shěn shòu hóng

qiān lǐ zuò yuǎn kè
千 里 作 远 客，

wǔ gēng sī gù xiāng
五 更 思 故 乡。

hán yā shù shēng qǐ
寒 鸦 数 声 起，

chuāng wài yuè rú shuāng
窗 外 月 如 霜。

 赏析

这是一首思乡诗。"千里""远客"点明诗人已离家千里之外。凌晨五更时分，诗人已无法安眠，寒鸦声声，月明似霜，更增添了诗人天涯羁旅的愁思。

第十四单元

chén dú duì yùn　　 èr shí qī
晨 读 对 韵（二 十 七）

táng
唐（ɑng）

míng duì àn　hù duì chuāng　dà hǎi duì cháng jiāng
明 对 暗，户 对 窗，大 海 对 长 江。

lóng fēi duì fèng wǔ　wēi yǔ duì xié yáng
龙 飞 对 凤 舞，微 雨 对 斜 阳。

shēn yuàn luò　xiǎo chí táng
深 院 落，小 池 塘。

shuǐ sè duì shān guāng
水 色 对 山 光。

bái làng huā qiān duǒ　qīng tiān yàn yì háng
白 浪 花 千 朵，青 天 雁 一 行。

fēng hán cuì zhú juān juān jìng
风 含 翠 竹 娟 娟 净，

yǔ yì hóng lián rǎn rǎn xiāng
雨 浥 红 莲 冉 冉 香。

chén dú duì yùn　èr shí bā
晨 读 对 韵（二十八）

táng
唐（ang）

gāo duì xià　duǎn duì cháng　jìn sòng duì suí táng
高 对 下，短 对 长，晋 宋 对 隋 唐 ①。

jiā bīn duì hǎo yǒu　nà hǎn duì páng huáng
嘉 宾 对 好 友，呐 喊 对 彷 徨 ②。

chí biān liǔ　mò shàng sāng　jú lǜ duì chéng huáng
池 边 柳，陌 上 桑。橘 绿 对 橙 黄。

hǎi wéi lóng shì jiè　yún shì hè jiā xiāng
海 为 龙 世 界，云 是 鹤 家 乡。

shì shì dòng míng jiē xué wen
世 事 洞 明 皆 学 问，

rén qíng liàn dá jí wén zhāng
人 情 练 达 即 文 章 ③。

注释

① 晋宋：晋指东晋（317—420），宋指南朝宋（420—479）。
② 呐喊：鲁迅先生的小说集名。彷徨：鲁迅先生的小说集名。
③ 引自《红楼梦》第5回。大意为：丰富的生活阅历、良好的人际交往是做好学问和写好文章的重要条件。

有形状的节日

（中国台湾）刘正盛

弟弟说

节日是有形状的。

"什么形状？"

"中秋节是圆形的，

端午节是三角形的，

春节是长方形的。"

"怎么说？"

"中秋节吃月饼，

端午节吃粽子。"

nà chūn jié chī shén me
"那春节吃什么？"

chūn jié ná hóng bāo
"春节拿红包！"

duì ya
对呀！

tiān cái dì di
天才弟弟！

赏析

　　每个节日都有着不同的庆祝方式。诗人巧妙地借用弟弟的口吻，形象地用各种形状来诠释每个节日的习俗，多么巧妙呀！

chuí yī shang
捶 衣 裳

◎ mín jiān tóng yáo
◎ 民 间 童 谣

xiǎo gū niang
小 姑 娘，

chuí yī shang
捶 衣 裳，

bàng chui gē zài shí tái shang
棒 槌 搁 在 石 台 上，

yī shang liàng zài zhú gān shang
衣 裳 晾 在 竹 竿 上。

sù jiàn dé jiāng
宿 建 德 江

（唐）孟 浩 然
táng mèng hào rán

yí zhōu bó yān zhǔ
移 舟 泊 烟 渚 ①，

rì mù kè chóu xīn
日 暮 客 愁 新 ②。

yě kuàng tiān dī shù
野 旷 天 低 树，

jiāng qīng yuè jìn rén
江 清 月 近 人 ③。

①移舟：摇船。烟渚：暮色中烟霭笼罩的小岛。渚，水中小块陆地。

②客愁：作客他乡之愁，即旅愁。新：愁绪新添，新愁续旧愁的意思。

③月近人：江中月影因水清而离人更近。

诗人以"愁"统领全篇，前两句写日暮移舟，客居他乡，又添新愁。后两句写景，意境陡升，表达了诗人心随明月的情怀。全诗情景相生、意味深长。

第十五单元

chén dú duì yùn èr shí jiǔ
晨 读 对 韵（二 十 九）

gēng
庚（eng ing）

shēn duì qiǎn zhòng duì qīng dàn yuè duì shū xīng
深 对 浅，重 对 轻，淡 月 对 疏 星。

léi míng duì diàn shǎn jiǔ yǔ duì xīn qíng
雷 鸣 对 电 闪，久 雨 对 新 晴。

yā zuǐ shòu māo tóu yīng
鸭 嘴 兽，猫 头 鹰。

zǐ yàn duì huáng yīng
紫 燕 对 黄 莺。

hú píng liǎng àn kuò jiāng shàng shù fēng qīng
湖 平 两 岸 阔，江 上 数 峰 青。

chūn shuǐ chuán rú tiān shàng zuò
春 水 船 如 天 上 坐，

qiū shān rén zài huà zhōng xíng
秋 山 人 在 画 中 行。

晨 读 对 韵（三 十）

庚（eng ing）

昏 对 旦，晦 对 明，久 别 对 重 逢。

批 评 对 赞 许，模 范 对 典 型。

杏 花 雨，杨 柳 风。

有 影 对 无 声。

读 书 破 万 卷，落 笔 超 群 英。

海 到 无 边 天 作 岸，

山 登 绝 顶 我 为 峰。

quán dōu zhī dào de zuǒ xī yà
全 都 知 道 的 佐 西 亚

bō lán dù wéi mǔ
[波兰] 杜 维 姆

dǒng la
懂 啦，

dǒng la
懂 啦，

wǒ yǐ jīng dǒng de gòu
我 已 经 懂 得 够

duō la
多 啦，

shá wǒ dōu zhī dào
啥 我 都 知 道：

wǒ bù zhī dào de hái yǒu
我 不 知 道 的 还 有

shén me
什 么！

mā ma kāi kǒu wèn zuǒ xī yà
妈 妈 开 口 问 佐 西 亚：

wǒ de nǚ ér ya
"我 的 女 儿 呀？

shéi ya shéi shì xiǎo shǎ guā
谁 呀 谁 是 小 傻 瓜？"

zuǒ xī yà dāng rán hái shì yí
佐 西 亚 当 然 还 是 一

jù huà
句 话，

duì mā ma tǐng shén qì de huí dá
对 妈 妈 挺 神 气 地 回 答：

shì wǒ ya
"是 我 呀！"

wéi wéi yì
（韦 苇 译）

赏析　可爱的孩子，妈妈的一个小小的圈套就让你掉了进去，而你却全不知道！短短的几行诗，让一个可爱、天真的佐西亚跃然于纸上。佐西亚是不是个"小傻瓜"呢？问问咱们的孩子吧！

小姑娘

◎ 民间童谣

小姑娘，会梳头，

一梳梳到麦子熟。

麦子磨成面，

芝麻榨成油，

黄瓜爬满架，

茄子打提溜。

sòng líng chè shàng rén
送 灵 澈 上 人 ①

（唐）刘 长 卿

cāng cāng zhú lín sì
苍 苍 竹 林 寺 ②，

yǎo yǎo zhōng shēng wǎn
杳 杳 钟 声 晚 ③。

hè lì dài xié yáng
荷 笠 带 斜 阳 ④，

qīng shān dú guī yuǎn
青 山 独 归 远 。

① 灵澈：著名诗僧。
② 竹林寺：《舆图备考》"镇江黄鹤山有鹤林寺，旧名竹林寺。"
③ 杳杳：深远的样子，远去状。
④ 荷：承担，负担。笠：笠帽。

这是一首送别诗，为我们刻画了精美如画的送别情景。前两行用"苍苍""杳杳"点明了上人归去的时间和去处。后两句犹如特写，刻画了灵澈越走越远，而诗人伫立目送、依依不舍的场景，表达了朋友间真挚的情谊，也表现出灵澈归山时清寂淡泊的风度。

第十六单元

chén dú duì yùn sān shí yī
晨读对韵（三十一）

dōng
东（ong iong）

yún duì yǔ xià duì dōng wǎn zhào duì qíng kōng
云对雨，夏对冬，晚照对晴空。

lái hóng duì qù yàn wén zhú duì wǔ sōng
来鸿对去燕，文竹对武松①。

tiān hào hào rì róng róng
天浩浩，日融融。

bì yě duì cāng qióng
碧野对苍穹。

jiāng liú tiān dì wài shān sè yǒu wú zhōng
江流天地外，山色有无中。

jiē tiān lián yè wú qióng bì
接天莲叶无穷碧，

yìng rì hé huā bié yàng hóng
映日荷花别样红。

注释　① 文竹对武松：植物名对人名，这是一个无情对。

晨 读 对 韵（三 十 二）
chén dú duì yùn sān shí èr

东（ong iong）
dōng

rén duì yì sè duì tōng zhuó yuè duì píng yōng
仁 对 义，塞 对 通，卓 越 对 平 庸。

gāo gē duì tòng yǐn kāng kǎi duì cóng róng
高 歌 对 痛 饮，慷 慨 对 从 容。

sān chǐ jiàn liù jūn gōng
三 尺 剑，六 钧 弓。

hú běi duì shān dōng
湖 北 对 山 东。

bié lái cāng hǎi shì yǔ bà mù tiān zhōng
别 来 沧 海 事，语 罢 暮 天 钟 ①。

shuǐ rú bì yù shān rú dài
水 如 碧 玉 山 如 黛，

yún xiǎng yī shang huā xiǎng róng
云 想 衣 裳 花 想 容。

① 选自唐代诗人李益《喜见外弟又言别》。

183

méi yǒu yì sōu chuán néng xiàng yì běn shū
没 有 一 艘 船 能 像 一 本 书

měi guó   dí jīn sēn
[美 国] 狄 金 森

méi yǒu yì sōu chuán néng xiàng yì běn shū
没 有 一 艘 船 能 像 一 本 书

yě méi yǒu yì pǐ jùn mǎ néng xiàng
也 没 有 一 匹 骏 马 能 像

yí yè tiào yuè zhe de shī háng nà yàng
一 页 跳 跃 着 的 诗 行 那 样 ——

bǎ rén dài wǎng yuǎn fāng
把 人 带 往 远 方。

zhè qú dào zuì qióng de rén yě néng zǒu
这 渠 道 最 穷 的 人 也 能 走

bú bì wèi tōng xíng shuì shāng shén
不 必 为 通 行 税 伤 神

zhè shì hé děng jié jiǎn de chē
这 是 何 等 节 俭 的 车 ——

chéng zài zhe rén de líng hún
承 载 着 人 的 灵 魂。

jiāng fēng yì
（江 枫 译）

赏析　　书是什么——文中通过一个形象的比喻,说明了书给人带来希望,把人带往远方。读起来生动形象,具体可感。

shéi gēn wǒ wán
谁 跟 我 玩

mín jiān tóng yáo
◎ 民 间 童 谣

shéi gēn wǒ wán　dǎ huǒ lián
谁 跟 我 玩，打 火 镰；

huǒ lián huā　mài tián guā
火 镰 花，卖 甜 瓜；

tián guā kǔ　mài dòu fu
甜 瓜 苦，卖 豆 腐；

dòu fu làn　mài jī dàn
豆 腐 烂，卖 鸡 蛋；

jī dàn xiāng　mài shēng jiāng
鸡 蛋 香，卖 生 姜；

shēng jiāng là　zào bǎo tǎ
生 姜 辣，造 宝 塔；

bǎo tǎ gāo　duò sān dāo
宝 塔 高，剁 三 刀；

sān dāo kuài　qiē qīng cài
三 刀 快，切 青 菜；

qīng cài qīng　shàng běi jīng
青 菜 青，上 北 京；

shàng běi jīng　qù gàn shá
上 北 京，去 干 啥？

yóu gù gōng　dēng jǐng shān
游 故 宫，登 景 山；

zài qù guàng guang yí hé yuán
再 去 逛 逛 颐 和 园。

chán
蝉

（唐）虞世南

chuí ruí yǐn qīng lù
垂緌饮清露①，

liú xiǎng chū shū tóng
流响出疏桐②。

jū gāo shēng zì yuǎn
居高声自远，

fēi shì jiè qiū fēng
非是藉秋风③。

① 垂緌：低垂着触须。
② 流响：指蝉长鸣不止。疏桐：繁茂而枝干分披的梧桐。
③ 藉：凭借，依靠。

这是一首托物寓意的小诗。诗中盛赞了蝉的居高声远，不必受制于它物，表达了诗人的价值取向：君子应高风亮节，雍容不迫。

附录

sān zì jīng
三 字 经

1

rén zhī chū　　xìng běn shàn
人 之 初①，性 本 善②。

xìng xiāng jìn　　xí xiāng yuǎn
性 相 近③，习 相 远④。

gǒu bú jiào　　xìng nǎi qiān
苟 不 教⑤，性 乃 迁⑥。

jiào zhī dào　　guì yǐ zhuān
教 之 道⑦，贵 以 专⑧。

注释

① 初：初生，刚开始有生命。

② 性：指人的本性。

③ 相近：相去不远，差不多的意思。

④ 习：习染，长期在某种环境下养成的特性。远：相去太远，有很大的差别。

⑤ 苟：如果，假如。教：训导，教诲。

⑥ 迁：改变，变迁，这里指变坏。

⑦ 道：方法，道理。

⑧ 贵：最重要的。

2

xī mèng mǔ　　　 zé lín chǔ
昔 孟 母 ①，择 邻 处 ②。

zǐ bù xué　　　 duàn jī zhù
子 不 学 ③，断 机 杼 ④。

dòu yān shān　　　 yǒu yì fāng
窦 燕 山 ⑤，有 义 方 ⑥。

jiào wǔ zǐ　　　 míng jù yáng
教 五 子，　名 俱 扬。

① 孟母：孟子的母亲。

② 择：选择。处：居住。

③ 子：孟子。

④ 断：动词，割断。机杼：机，织机。杼，梭子。

⑤ 窦燕山：即窦禹钧，五代后晋人，他聘请名儒做儿子的老师，后来五个儿子都考中进士。

⑥ 义方：教育孩子的方法。

3

yǎng bú jiào　　fù zhī guò
养 不 教， 父 之 过 ①。

jiào bù yán　　shī zhī duò
教 不 严 ②， 师 之 惰 ③。

zǐ bù xué　　fēi suǒ yí
子 不 学， 非 所 宜 ④。

yòu bù xué　　lǎo hé wéi
幼 不 学， 老 何 为 ⑤。

注释

① 过：过错。
② 严：周密。
③ 惰：懒惰，这里指失职。
④ 宜：应该。
⑤ 何为：做什么。

4

yù bù zhuó　　bù chéng qì
玉 不 琢 ①, 不 成 器 ②。

rén bù xué　　bù zhī yì
人 不 学, 不 知 义 ③。

wéi rén zǐ　　fāng shào shí
为 人 子, 方 少 时 ④。

qīn shī yǒu　　xí lǐ yí
亲 师 友 ⑤,习 礼 仪。

① 琢:雕刻玉石。
② 器:器物。
③ 义:做人的道理。
④ 少时:小时候。
⑤ 亲:亲近。

5

xiāng jiǔ líng　　néng wēn xí
香 九 龄 ①，能 温 席。

xiào yú qīn　　suǒ dāng zhí
孝 于 亲，所 当 执 ②。

róng sì suì　　néng ràng lí
融 四 岁 ③，能 让 梨。

tì yú zhǎng　　yí xiān zhī
弟 于 长 ④，宜 先 知 ⑤。

shǒu xiào tì　　cì jiàn wén
首 孝 弟 ⑥，次 见 闻。

zhī mǒu shù　　shí mǒu wén
知 某 数，识 某 文。

注释

① 香：黄香，东汉人，博通经典，官至尚书令。
② 当执：应该做的。
③ 融：指孔融，东汉人。
④ 弟：同"悌"，指弟弟敬爱哥哥。
⑤ 知：明白。
⑥ 孝弟：孝顺父母，友爱兄长。弟，同"悌"。

6

yuē chūn xià　　　yuē qiū dōng　　　cǐ sì shí　　　yùn bù qióng
日春夏^①，日秋冬。此四时，运不穷^②。

yuē nán běi　　　yuē xī dōng　　　cǐ sì fāng　　　yìng hū zhōng
日南北，日西东。此四方，应乎中^③。

yuē shuǐ huǒ　　　mù jīn tǔ　　　cǐ wǔ xíng　　　běn hū shù
日水火，木金土。此五行^④，本乎数^⑤。

yuē rén yì　　　lǐ zhì xìn　　　cǐ wǔ cháng　　　bù róng wěn
日仁义，礼智信。此五常^⑥，不容紊^⑦。

注释

① 曰：这里是"称为""叫作"的意思，并有表示列举的作用。

② 运：运行，转动。

③ 应：相应，适应。

④ 五行：我国古代思想家认为"水火木金土"这五种物质是构成万物不可缺少的元素。

⑤ 本：根据，起源。数：是术数的简称，以阴阳五行生、克、共、化的道理，推测人事吉凶，叫术数，也叫数命、数理、命理等。

⑥ 五常：指仁义礼智信。

⑦ 紊：杂乱。

7

gāo zēng zǔ　　fù ér shēn
高曾祖①，父而身②。

shēn ér zǐ　　zǐ ér sūn
身而子，子而孙。

zì zǐ sūn　　zhì xuán zēng
自子孙，至玄曾③。

nǎi jiǔ zú　　rén zhī lún
乃九族④，人之伦⑤。

注释

①高：高祖，祖父的祖父母。曾：曾祖，祖父的父母。祖：祖
父母。

②而：到。身：自身。

③玄：玄孙，孙辈的孙辈。曾：曾孙，孙辈的子女。

④九族：从高祖到玄孙共九世，称为九族。

⑤伦：序，指尊卑老幼的秩序。

8

dú shǐ zhě　kǎo shí lù
读 史 者，考 实 录 ①。

tōng gǔ jīn　ruò qīn mù
通 古 今，若 亲 目 ②。

kǒu ér sòng　xīn ér wéi
口 而 诵，心 而 惟 ③。

zhāo yú sī　xī yú sī
朝 于 斯，夕 于 斯。

注释

① 考：考证。
② 亲目：亲眼目睹。
③ 惟：思维，思考。

9

xī zhòng ní
昔 仲 尼①，师 项 橐②。

gǔ shèng xián shàng qín xué
古 圣 贤， 尚 勤 学。

zhào zhōng lìng dú lǔ lún
赵 中 令③，读 鲁 论④。

bǐ jì shì xué qiě qín
彼 既 仕⑤，学 且 勤。

注释

① 仲尼：孔子名丘，字仲尼，春秋时代鲁国人。

② 项橐：七岁时为孔子的老师。

③ 赵中令：赵普，宋朝中书令。

④ 鲁论：书名，《论语》有三种本子，是《鲁论》、《齐论》、《古论》。现在我们通常读的是《鲁论》。

⑤ 仕：做官。

10

<ruby>披<rt>pī</rt></ruby><ruby>蒲<rt>pú</rt></ruby><ruby>编<rt>biān</rt></ruby>①，<ruby>削<rt>xiāo</rt></ruby><ruby>竹<rt>zhú</rt></ruby><ruby>简<rt>jiǎn</rt></ruby>②。

<ruby>彼<rt>bǐ</rt></ruby><ruby>无<rt>wú</rt></ruby><ruby>书<rt>shū</rt></ruby>，<ruby>且<rt>qiě</rt></ruby><ruby>知<rt>zhī</rt></ruby><ruby>勉<rt>miǎn</rt></ruby>③。

<ruby>头<rt>tóu</rt></ruby><ruby>悬<rt>xuán</rt></ruby><ruby>梁<rt>liáng</rt></ruby>④，<ruby>锥<rt>zhuī</rt></ruby><ruby>刺<rt>cì</rt></ruby><ruby>股<rt>gǔ</rt></ruby>⑤。

<ruby>彼<rt>bǐ</rt></ruby><ruby>不<rt>bú</rt></ruby><ruby>教<rt>jiào</rt></ruby>，<ruby>自<rt>zì</rt></ruby><ruby>勤<rt>qín</rt></ruby><ruby>苦<rt>kǔ</rt></ruby>。

注释

① 披:分开。蒲编:用蒲草编织的席子。汉代路温舒家境贫寒,但仍然刻苦读书,传说他在湖边牧羊时,取蒲草编席,然后把他借来的《尚书》抄在席子上阅读。

② 竹简:用竹削成薄片,在竹简上写字。传说汉代公孙弘在竹林中放猪时,把青竹削成竹片,向人借来《春秋》抄了读。

③ 勉:勤勉。

④ 头悬梁:传说汉代的孔敬常读书到深夜,唯恐打瞌睡,把头发用绳子系住,挂在屋梁上。

⑤ 锥刺股:传说战国时的苏秦日夜苦读,在瞌睡时,用锥子刺自己的大腿,痛醒了再继续学习。股,大腿。

11

rú náng yíng   rú yìng xuě
如 囊 萤①，如 映 雪②。

jiā suī pín   xué bú chuò
家 虽 贫， 学 不 辍③。

rú fù xīn   rú guà jiǎo
如 负 薪④，如 挂 角⑤。

shēn suī láo   yóu kǔ zhuó
身 虽 劳， 犹 苦 卓⑥。

① 囊萤：晋朝人车胤，家贫，夏天夜读时，没有点灯的油，传说他捉来萤火虫放进一只薄纱囊中以照明。

② 映雪：晋朝人孙康，家贫，冬天夜读时，没有点灯的油，于是到户外，借助雪的反光以照明。

③ 辍：中止，停顿。

④ 负薪：薪，柴火。西汉人朱买臣，年轻时靠打柴为生，即便如此，仍坚持读书，在砍柴时，经常将书放在树下随时阅读。砍柴归来，将书悬在担头，边走边读。

⑤ 挂角：隋朝人李密，幼时替人放牛，常常坐在牛背上读书，而把剩余的书挂在牛角上。

⑥ 卓：坚卓，卓越。

12

sū lǎo quán　　 èr shí qī
苏 老 泉 ①，二 十 七。

shǐ fā fèn　　dú shū jí
始 发 愤，　读 书 籍。

bǐ jì lǎo　　yóu huǐ chí
彼 既 老，　犹 悔 迟 ②。

ěr xiǎo shēng　　yí zǎo sī
尔 小 生 ③，宜 早 思 ④。

① 苏老泉：苏洵，字明允，号老泉，宋代著名文学家，"唐宋八大家"之一，苏轼之父。

② 犹悔迟：还后悔太晚。

③ 小生：后辈。

④ 宜：应该。

13

ruò liáng hào　　　bā　shí　èr
若 梁 灏 ①，八 十 二。

duì　dà　tíng　　kuí　duō　shì
对 大 廷 ②，魁 多 士 ③。

bǐ　jì　chéng　zhòng chēng　yì
彼 既 成 ，众 称 异 ④。

ěr　xiǎo shēng　　yí　　lì　zhì
尔 小 生 ，宜 立 志。

注释

　　① 梁灏：北宋人，字太素，二十三岁考中状元，四十二岁那年因为疾病突然死去。所谓梁灏八十二岁中状元事，系误传。
　　② 大廷：朝廷的意思。
　　③ 魁：为首的，居第一位的。
　　④ 称异：认为奇特。

14

yíng bā suì　　néng yǒng shī
莹 八 岁①，能 咏 诗。

mì qī suì　　néng fù qí
泌 七 岁②，能 赋 棋。

bǐ yǐng wù　　rén chēng qí
彼 颖 悟③，人 称 奇。

ěr yòu xué　　dāng xiào zhī
尔 幼 学，　当 效 之④。

注释

① 莹：指北魏人祖莹，传说他八岁就能朗诵《诗经》。
② 泌：指李泌，传说他七岁时曾应唐玄宗命作《棋赋》。
③ 颖悟：聪明，敏捷。
④ 效：效仿。

15

cài wén jī　　néng biàn qín
蔡 文 姬 ①，能 辨 琴。

xiè dào yùn　　néng yǒng yín
谢 道 韫 ②，能 咏 吟。

táng liú yàn　　fāng qī suì
唐 刘 晏 ③，方 七 岁。

jǔ shén tóng　　zuò zhèng zì
举 神 童，作 正 字。

bǐ suī yòu　　shēn yǐ shì
彼 虽 幼，身 已 仕。

yǒu wéi zhě　　yì ruò shì
有 为 者，亦 若 是 ④。

① 蔡文姬：东汉人，从小喜爱读书，精于音律。
② 谢道韫：晋朝女文学家，诗才敏捷，是当时著名的才女。
③ 刘晏：唐代曹州人。
④ 亦若是：也像这样。

16

quǎn shǒu yè jī sī chén
犬 守 夜，鸡 司 晨①。

gǒu bù xué hé wéi rén
苟 不 学，曷 为 人②。

cán tǔ sī fēng niàng mì
蚕 吐 丝，蜂 酿 蜜。

rén bù xué bù rú wù
人 不 学，不 如 物。

注释

① 司：管理，掌握。
② 曷：怎么。

亲近母语：培育有中国根基的世界公民

我们是谁

我们是一群热爱母语，热爱童年的人。我们有一个共同的名字：亲近母语。我们秉持"亲近母语，呵护童年"的核心理念，致力于培育有中国根基的世界公民。

我们在做什么

针对当前语文教育忽视儿童生命体验，内容短小轻薄的不足，我们致力于为中国儿童提供最专业的儿童阅读和儿童母语教育方案。

我们的机构

亲近母语研究院——致力于为中国儿童提供最专业的儿童阅读和儿童母语教育方案。

亲近母语学堂——面向3-12岁儿童提供专业的母语教育。目前仅在南京、扬州开设，是亲近母语教育理念的完整体现。已形成以母语学习、中国文化、儿童哲学课程为核心的独特课程体系。

我们可以提供哪些服务

针对学校渠道，我们向区县、实验学校和公益机构提供儿童阅读和儿童母语教育的全解决方案。包括课程解决方案、教师培训计划、课题研究指导、书香校园建设指导等。

针对家长，我们开设父母学堂，通过网上讲座与实地活动相结合的方式对家长进行儿童阅读与儿童母语教育的咨询。

我们的课题研究

亲近母语实验发端于2000年，已历经三个五年规划的实验和研究。2003年亲近母语课题被立项为全国教育科学"十五"规划课题，2007年荣获江苏省第二届教育科学优秀成果一等奖，《中国教育报》《人民教育》等专业媒体多次刊发对亲近母语课题实验的介绍。

我们的课程

亲近母语课题经过十余年的探索，研发了以儿童诵读、主题阅读、整本书阅读、图画书阅读、儿童写作为核心的实验课程。并有相应的课程用书和推荐书目。

我们的教师培训

中国儿童阅读论坛——大陆和华语地区最有影响的儿童阅读论坛，被称为"点灯人"的聚会。

儿童母语教育论坛——国内儿童母语教育的高端平台。

种子教师研习营——培养有文学底蕴、视野开阔、研究能力强的儿童阅读种子教师。

怎样找到我们

通讯地址：江苏省南京市栖霞区紫东路1号紫东国际创意园E座亲近母语研究院

电话：025—68710080　　　网址：www.qjmy.cn

HOLY CROSS SCHOOL

UNDERSTANDING THE INQUISITION

FRANCISCUS WILLETT

Understanding
the
Inquisition

HOLY CROSS PRESS
No. Easton, Massachusetts

Library of Congress Catalog Number: 68-30958

PRINTED IN THE U.S.A. BY *Theo. Gaus' Sons, Inc.*,
BROOKLYN, N. Y.

CONTENTS

4964

1

The Inquisition in True Focus

1

AFTER TREKKING THROUGH his world for long millenia man has finally come to appreciate the ideal of tolerance. This does not mean that tolerance is universal or even widespread today, for there is too much evidence to the contrary. Man is still ready to persecute and even kill those with another political system, another philosophy or religion, or even another color of skin. Man is so prone to prejudice that he can discriminate against those who believe different than he, or dress different, or live different. Half the world lives under communism, a system built on class intolerance. We in America, proclaiming ourselves "the land of the free," are no strangers to hatred because of race and national origin, nor is religious intolerance unknown to us. In spite of all this, modern man has finally arrived at a concept of tolerance and an appreciation of its ideal. Slowly, but inexorably, the force of this idea of tolerance is re-shaping our thinking and even our institutions. We are learning that "different" need not mean "enemy."

If this is so, why should there be a book about the system of intolerance known as the Inquisition? Would it not be better to let it remain buried in history's graveyard? It is important to understand the Inquisition for several reasons. Even though the Inquisition is long dead it has caused misunderstanding and intolerance of the Catholic Church even into our own day. To understand it truly, in its historical perspective, is to clear the air in some small way of the miasma of hatred and intolerance. Strangely, few books have been written about this unfortunate medieval institution. Those that were written are filled with a hatred that matches the Inquisition at its worst. Some have been badly informed, not understanding the forces that went into shaping the Inquisition. One or two, incredibly, have been written defending this system of intolerance and persecution.

The study of the Inquisition is important, too, so that we may have historical perspective for judging the present and planning the future. Sometimes it seems that we make no progress at all, that man simply changes one folly for another as the centuries roll. Careful historical study shows us that we are progressing, even if slowly and painfully. We *are* working out our destiny, through much effort and suffering. Our study of history gives us courage to continue the work of perfecting the world in which we live and the human nature we all share. Sometimes we fall back, as we see so intensely in the savage inhumanity of the Nazi's mass murder of the Jews, a barbarism unthinkable at the time of the Inquisition. History tells us that such lapses into our uncivilized past can be averted, that the general thrust of man's struggle is upward.

Most history textbooks devote a paragraph or two to the Inquisition without ever assessing its effects upon history. Yet, it had tremendous influence on the course of events so that its effects remain even to this day. Some of these effects will be assessed as the story and development of the Inquisition unrolls.

Finally, we need to study the Inquisition to make sure that nothing like it ever occurs again. The Catholic Church renounced the Inquisition and all use of force in the Second Vatican Council, in the *Declaration on Religious Freedom*. It announced and adopted a set of principles in which persecution could never find a place. It is for all mankind to learn from the errors of the past so that a better future may come about. Progress is not inevitable. Each step upward in civilization must be earned.

2

What was the Inquisition? It was a system of seeking out and punishing those who held religious views differing from the orthodox Catholic faith. It was especially interested in organized secret sects, such as the Albigenses and the Waldenses, described later in this chapter. It had its greatest influence and power roughly from 1250 A.D. to 1350 A.D., and flourished especially in Italy, France, and Spain. Other countries, notably modern Germany and Czechoslovakia were also touched by the Inquisition, but it was never established in England. Some of the famous cases of the Inquisition are those of Galileo, Joan of Arc, Savonarola, and John Huss. Its secret courts formed a mesh in which a heretic (one who held unorthodox doctrines) was almost sure to be caught.

In the popular imagination of today the Inquisition is connected with the cruel death of burning at the stake. Most people know that torture was freely used to extract confessions. In the 1950's there was in the Times Square section of New York a "Believe It or Not Museum," operated by the famous Robert Ripley. In the basement were displayed a large number of instruments of torture. There were racks, used to pull a man's body until the bones came from the sockets. There were pincers, to be heated and applied to those who stubbornly refused to confess. A large number of other instruments, for even more horrible purposes, were also displayed, with a sign explaining that they were used by the Inquisition. While it is true that the Inquisition did use instruments of torture, most of these shown in the Ripley museum were never used. In the proper place the question of torture will be discussed. It was not universally used, and while horrible enough, the tortures applied to heretics or suspected heretics were not as cruel as those shown by Ripley. Nor were burnings at the stake as common as popular imagination today has it. Too many did die by this terrible means, but the number was nowhere as great as is usually supposed.

The entire question of the Inquisition is not a simple one, for often the heretics were a great menace to society. The Inquisition itself was often used by kings and rulers to get rid of political enemies. It is only by understanding the times that spawned the Inquisition that we can see it clearly and truly, and learn its lessons for today.

First, the age itself was cruel. Many of the peoples of Europe were removed from barbarism by only a few hundred years, and many of their old customs survived. Criminal law provided for such punishments as branding, cutting off of hands, burning alive, tearing apart with horses, immersion in caldrons of heated oil. Even light offenses were severely punished. A thief most often paid for his crime with his life. If fortunate, he escaped with having his hands cut off. In such an age the punishments applied by the Inquisition were moderate indeed, less than those normally applied by secular powers. This does not excuse the use of force by the Church, but it shows that the inquisitors were not wild, ravening beasts, but moderate men according to the standards of their times.

Second, it is important to understand that according to the political ideas of the times it was almost inevitable that the Church would undertake the Inquisition. Today most of the world has very clear ideas about the separation of church and state. In the ancient world it was common for rulers to insist that their people worship the approved gods. It was a way of controlling the populace, a quick unity within the country. It was common to punish those who introduced other religions, as witness the story of the prophet Daniel who was thrown to the lions because he would not accept the Babylonian gods. In 312 A.D. the emperor Constantine decreed toleration of the Christian religion, freeing it from three hundred years of persecution. By the year 325 the emperor was already interfering with the interior workings of the Church, calling for an ecumenical council to define the orthodox faith. The Church obliged, and produced the Nicene Creed. Soon, far from mere toleration, the Church had a favored place in the plan of the government and the ancient religions began to disappear in the lands controlled by the Roman Empire of the West. In the fifth century the government even fitfully persecuted followers of the Manichaean heresy. (St. Augustine for many years was a Manichaean before his conversion to the Church.) After the breakdown of the Roman empire almost all the people were Catholic. When the Frankish ruler became Catholic it was natural, according to his thinking and the customs of the times, that he should insist that all his subjects become Catholics also. As the world slipped into the Dark Ages the nations of Europe were all Catholic. It never occurred to anyone that he should be anything else than a member of the Church. Here, then, was a situation in which both rulers and people were all of the same religion, and that religion became as much a part of civic life as laws and taxes.

The development of the feudal system helped confuse the separate identity of Church and state. Feudalism developed after central government broke down upon the fall of the Roman Empire. Local lords became the owners of the land, which they gave for use to men of less power upon the promise of fealty. This was a promise to remain faithful to the lord and to furnish soldiers and arms for defense, and the payment of taxes. The essence of feudalism was an agreement. The lesser rulers, known as vassals, agreed to recognize the power of the lord, to give taxes for the land he released to them, and to furnish men to him for his army. The lord, in return, guaranteed their peace and protection. At the bottom of the feudal pyramid were the serfs, farmers bound to their land and owing taxes and services to their immediate lord. As centuries passed, this system of fiefs, as holdings granted by the lord were called, became very complicated. Nations arose, and kings were at the pinnacle of the feudal system. The ruler of England, for instance, was called "England," for in theory he was the country and owned every inch of land, only granting it as fiefs to his vassals. Among these were abbots and bishops, who were often lesser lords of vast territories. As vassals of the king they owed him fealty for these lands. By virtue of their state as churchmen they owed loyalty to the pope. It was a confusing situation. For example, in the twelfth century the Archbishop of York was vassal to King Henry II for a large holding of lands in England. The Archbishop administered these lands the same as any other lord, receiving the income from the lands and paying his taxes and homage to the king. At the same time he was subject in the spiritual realm to the primate of all England, the Archbishop of Canterbury, and through Canterbury, to the Pope. There were times when these loyalties conflicted. They clashed in the twelfth century when Henry II was guilty of the assassination of Thomas Becket, the Archbishop of Canterbury. They conflicted in the sixteenth century, when Henry VIII separated the English church from Rome over the question of his divorce from Queen Catherine.

While kingdoms remained weak because of the feudal

system, the power of the papacy grew. The Church was an organization that spanned feudal boundaries and reached to every part of Europe. Lords, vassals, and serfs all owed it allegiance. In 800 A.D. Pope Leo III inaugurated the Holy Roman Empire by crowning Charlemagne as emperor. The hope was that all christendom would eventually be united under one secular ruler as it was united under one spiritual ruler. This was not to be, and the Holy Roman Empire never consisted of more than Germany, Austria, parts of France and modern Czechoslovakia, and parts of Italy. It always remained weak and divided. Yet its existence proclaimed the power of the pope, who alone could crown the emperor.

Pope Gregory VII, also known as Hildebrand, greatly strengthened the power of the pope by his struggle with the Holy Roman Emperor Henry IV in the eleventh century. The quarrel between the two showed clearly the dangers of too great cooperation between church and state. Henry insisted on the right of appointing bishops, abbots, and other ecclesiastical officials. Rulers had done this for long years. It seemed reasonable to them, for the bishops were holders and administrators of vast lands and were vassals of the king. Gregory, however, insisted that the Church alone had the right to choose and appoint bishops. After a sharp struggle the emperor Henry was brought temporarily to his knees at Canossa in 1077, where he awaited outside the castle where the pope was staying, begging for release from the sentence of excommunication. Although Henry later seemed to triumph, the principle of the rights of the papacy was established by this incident.

Innocent III, pope from 1198 to 1216, brought the papacy to its highest point. Theologians had already laid the groundwork. They developed the idea of "two swords," spiritual and temporal. The Church, they said, controlled them both.

"Both the spiritual and the temporal swords belong to the Church," wrote St. Bernard, "the latter to be drawn for the Church, the former by the Church." Innocent III reasoned that as he was the Vicar of Christ, he had the authority and the duty to intervene and pass judgment wherever there was a moral question. Since almost everything has a moral dimension he found ample opportunity to intervene in temporal affairs of governments. Perhaps his most famous intervention occurred in 1208. A disputed election of the Archbishop was referred to Rome. Innocent persuaded the canons who were the electors to choose a candidate whom he put forward, Stephen Langton. King John refused to recognize the election and Innocent retaliated by placing all of England under interdict. This meant that nowhere in England could the sacraments be administered or Mass celebrated. The people, of course, were anxious for the lifting of the interdict, desiring the ministrations of the Church. John held out a year and a half, but was forced to capitulate when he was excommunicated and Innocent threatened to depose him. In 1213 John gave England to Innocent and received it back from him as a fief, so that he and all his successors theoretically held power in England as papel fiefs.

This, then, was the society in which the Inquisition arose. It was a society in which great emphasis was placed on conformity and unity. There was confusion on the proper roles of Church and state. It was a time when the law was harsh and cruel. An outbreak like the Inquisition would almost inevitably arise whenever a major heresy arose. The coming of the stubborn Albigensian, or Cathar, heresy brought all these forces together and the Inquisition was launched.

3

The Albigensian heresy, also known as Catharism, was the first great heresy to rend medieval Europe. About the year 1000 it seems to have spread from Bulgaria to northern Italy, and thence to France and northern Spain. It is called Albigensian because a hotbed of its adherents was in the town of Albi in southern France. It is also called Catharism from the word *cathar*, which means "purified." Its doctrines are almost identical with those of the Manichaean heresy which flourished in the fifth century. The resemblances are so great that we can only suppose that certain pockets of Manichaeism held out for hundreds of years. The doctrines were peculiar, a mixture of Eastern mysticism and perverted Christianity. It was an evil religion. If it had triumphed it would have wrecked or destroyed society. Oddly, it appealed to both the learned and the simple. It received allegiance from its adherents that led them to suffer persecution and death willingly.

Albigensianism saw two equal principles at work in the world, two gods, one of whom was good, the other evil. The good principle was called God; the evil principle, Satan. God was the creator of the eternal universe, spiritual and invisible in its nature. Satan was the creator of the material universe and everything in it. All matter, then, was evil, and the secret of salvation was to escape from visible matter. The Jehovah of the Old Testament was really Satan, and Christ came to overthrow Jehovah. To do this he did not take a body, because material bodies are evil. Instead, he was a phantasm, a spirit seeming to have a body. Through his presence in the world Christ overthrew the power of Satan-Jehovah and made it possible for men to escape his clutches if they became spiritual. They were saved through receiving the Spirit given by Christ, though this Spirit does not seem to be the Holy Spirit, the third person of the Trinity.

The Albigenses rejected all the sacraments since the sacraments operated through evil matter. They regarded bishops and priests of their sect as revered teachers, but they gave them no authority over the members. They believed that souls were reincarnated in other bodies until at last they were purified enough to come before God. They followed simple rituals and came together regularly for instruction, teaching, and encouragement. There were two classes of Albigenses, the simple and the Perfected. The Perfected were those who received the great sacrament, the consolamentum. Since being one of the Perfected placed heavy obligations on the follower it was common to put off receiving the consolamentum until the deathbed. It was usual for the simple Albigensian to enter into "the covenant." By this he agreed to undergo the consolamentum on his deathbed, even if he should have lost his power of speech.

The consolamentum took a very simple form. It could be performed anywhere, but it was generally performed in meetings of the group where there were enough of the sect to make local congregations. One of the Perfected, usually a bishop, presided at the ceremony. The one desiring initiation presented himself before the elders, where the following interrogation took place.

"Brother, do you wish to give yourself to our faith?"

"Pray God for this sinner that I make a good end and become a good Christian."

"May God make you a good Christian and bring you to a good end. Do you give yourself to God and the Gospel?"

"I do," replied the one being perfected.

"Do you promise that in the future you will eat no meat, eggs, cheese, nor any food except from water and wood? Do you promise not to swear, lie, or be unchaste? Do you promise not to go alone when you can have a comrade? Do you promise not to abandon the faith for fear of fire or water or any death."

"I do."

At this point the minister placed the book of the Gospels

upon the head of the new Abigensian Perfected and read the first verses of the Gospel according to St. John. This completed the ceremony of the consolamentum. The newly perfected man was given a "sacred thread" which he always wore. Those present finally exchanged the kiss of peace.

The reference to being chaste in the ceremony meant much more than the Christian virtue of chastity. It required the Perfected to refrain from marriage. Indeed, all followers of the sect were urged not to marry nor bring children into the world, for in so doing they were furthering the kingdom of Satan. It is apparent that if this heresy had triumphed the very future and survival of the human race would have been in peril. The ceremony also indicates several other characteristics of the Albigenses. Meat or any products derived from animals, such as eggs or cheese, were avoided because living matter was evil. These men also believed that human souls were reborn into animal bodies if they were not ready for the peace of perfection. For some reasons they excepted fish, which it was lawful for them to eat.

It can be seen that the external life of the Albigensian heretic was a model of restraint, so that often he could be detected because his life was more exemplary than those about him. He refused to swear or take oaths. He fasted three times a week. He was sober and chaste in his life. St. Bernard, who tried unsuccessfully to wipe them out by conversion said, "If you interrogate them, nothing can be more Christian; as to their conversation, nothing could be less reprehensible, and what they speak, they prove by their deeds. As for the morals of the heretic, he strikes no one, his cheeks are pale with fasting, and he labors hard for his livelihood." In other words, a heretic could be recognized because he acted more Christian than Christians!

The Albigenses grew at a remarkable pace. Many towns were almost entirely converted to this heresy. The entire province of Languedoc in southern France, including such large towns as Toulouse, Carcassonne, and Narbonne, was practically in the hands of the Albigenses. In the thirteenth century perhaps half of Milan and Florence were adherents of the heretics. The Albigenses were great spreaders of their doctrines. They worked at friendships long and hard, and when the right moment presented itself they explained their doctrines. They even adopted the practice of dropping their tracts and writings along the wayside. Since most of the people could not read these tracts were often taken to the parish priests. It speaks ill of the state of the clergy that often the priests were converted to the heresy through the reading of these tracts.

Indeed, it was the sad state of the clergy that made Albigensianism and other heresies attractive to many and greatly aided their spread. Although popes had made great efforts to strengthen the quality of bishops and priests the fact is that too many of them were ignorant men of lax lives. This was the time when Europe was emerging from the long night of the Dark Ages, but all segments of society, including the Church, had been brutalized by the breakdown of law and order after the fall of Rome. The gentle light of the rising civilization of the Middle Ages did not sweep away all darkness at once. Most of the lower clergy were poorly educated, unable even to preach a sermon. They received but little help or encouragement from their bishops, who were feudal lords, and often less educated than they. Bishoprics and abbacies were sought by men who were often worldly-minded, wanting the secular power the office gave them. Bishops often did not live in their dioceses, and sometimes but rarely visited them. Even the papacy was fought for as a rich prize and important families sought to place their relatives upon Peter's throne. When the temporal power of the Church was so stressed it is not remarkable that unworthy men were to be found throughout the Church. The great wonder is that the Church continued to survive in face of all the corruption that surrounded it. But, true to the promise of Christ its Founder, it remained firm upon its rock and even produced great saints, flowers amidst the cockle. Lest this picture seem too black we should remember the simple people of Europe who looked to the invisible fabric of the Church, the part that was the spotless Bride of Christ, rather than to the dust that smeared the visible pilgrim Church. For most of them, their faith never wavered and their lives drew holiness from the sacramental system of the Church.

It was in this climate that the Albigenses flourished. Though it had its simple beauties, there were terrible parts of the heresy, too. In a religious system where marriage was a worse fault than adultery or fornication, abuses and orgies must be expected. These did occur, though perhaps not as often as the orthodox whispered. Much worse was the disregard for human life. It was common for those who received the consolamentum to begin the starvation fast known as the *endura*. Since life was wicked it was virtue to destroy it. Men and women who received the consolamentum on their deathbed, fulfilling their covenant, were sometimes or even often smothered with a pillow or began the *endura* themselves. Suicide was common among the Albigenses.

On balance, the heresy was an ugly and perverted thing, an enemy of man as well as of the Church. It is easy to see the results of widespread Albigensianism. Its attitude toward marriage threatened the survival of the human race. Its hatred of the material universe indicates that progress would never have occurred. Why try to brighten or improve a life that is not worth living anyway? For these reasons it is well that the Albigenses lost their struggle for survival.

4

A lesser heresy the Inquisition had to contend with was that of the Waldenses. It takes its name after Peter Waldo, a rich merchant of Lyons, in France, during the last half of the twelfth century. After Waldo had made his fortune he turned his attention to the study of theology. He commissioned scholars to translate the Bible into his native French, and it was this volume that was the basis of his self-conducted studies. The absolute poverty of Jesus and the communal life of the early Church struck him forcibly, so that Waldo, the rich merchant, disposed of all his wealth. He walked about Lyons and the neighboring villages in humble dress, explaining to the people the good news of the Gospel as he understood it. Soon he collected a small band of disciples who worked with him and shared his views. They were easily recognizable by their simple dress and the sandals they wore upon their feet. They called themselves "The Poor Men of Lyons."

Since they were only simple men, despite their former wealth, they were soon over their heads in handling theological questions. The Poor Men went beyond simple witness to Christian simplicity and began to give in to the people's desire to hear them speak on other topics. In short order they fell into heresy. Perhaps the admiration of the people led them to pride, especially when the lives of the Poor Men were compared so favorably with the worldly lives of too many bishops and prisests. They soon began to attack the clergy for the abuses in their lives. Their first error was to claim that the Mass and the sacraments were worthless when administered by priests in the state of sin. This was a dangerous teaching, for it called into question every Mass, every confession, even every baptism, since no one could know the interior state of another, and too often there were grave reasons for suspecting the worst. The errors began to pile up as the Poor Men claimed that only God, not the visible Church, should be obeyed; that the entire doctrine of indulgences was false, that the right to preach was granted to every man. Within a few years the Waldenses, as the Poor Men came to be known, were far removed from the orthodox Church in doctrine, and even farther in sympathy and spirit. By this time they had grown remarkably, spreading throughout France and even into northern Italy and Germany. The Church could no longer ignore them and they fell under the scrutiny of the Inquisition, which had come into existence about the same time as themselves.

It was these two heresies, then, the Albigenses and the Waldenses, that mainly occupied the interests of the Inquisition. They did not monopolize its attentions, however, for other aberrations, such as sorcery and witchcraft, the scandal of the Knights Templar, and the movement known as the "Spiritual Franciscans" also came under its notice. While we find little or nothing to be said in favor of the Inquisition we can find even less for the objects of its persecutions. These heresies and movements attacked not only the Church but also the state, and even our common human nature.

2

The Establishment of the Inquisition

1

THE CHURCH OBVIOUSLY HAS an interest in purity of doctrine. It has been entrusted with a message which it must impart, entire and uncorrupted. This concern goes back to apostolic times. Writing to Timothy, St. Paul uttered the first condemnation against heretics. "I commit to you this charge, my son Timothy," he writes, "that you may fight the good fight, having faith in a good conscience. Some, rejecting this, have made a shipwreck of the faith, among whom are Hymeneus and Alexander, whom I have delivered up to Satan that they may learn not to blaspheme." The question is not the right of the Church to insist on purity of doctrine, but the methods used against those who go contrary to it. From the earliest times the Church was opposed to the use of force, preferring to use moral persuasion in its place. St. John Chrysostom (345-407) perhaps put it best when he said, "To put a heretic to death would be to introduce upon the earth an inexpiable crime." Perhaps John had in mind the teaching of Christ that he had come to save sinners, not to destroy them.

There was persecution and even execution of heretics in the first centuries of Christianity, but these came about because the Roman emperors did not desire a divided Church and prosecuted heretics as civil criminals. The emperors Valentinian I and Theodosius I, called the Great, enacted legislation against heretics, decreeing exile and confiscation as penalties. The attitude of the Church toward the death sentence is best shown by the case of the Spanish bishop Priscillian. The teachings of Priscillian were condemned by the Council of Saragossa in 380. When his appeals to Rome were refused he was asked to appear before another council. Priscillian was unwilling to be judged by this council and appealed to the Emperor Maximus. The main accuser was another Spanish bishop named Ithacius. For a while St. Ambrose and St. Martin of Tours were successful in persuading Ithacius not to press his charges of heresy, since the emperor was likely to inflict a sentence of death. At length, however, Ithacius urged Maximus to pass sentence. Priscillian and six of his followers were burned alive in 385 by order of the emperor. There was great revulsion against this sentence and St. Martin was loud in his condemnation of Ithacius, as were Ambrose and Pope St. Damasus. Even the Spanish bishops who had condemned Priscillian's teachings had no stomach for this sort of thing and forced Ithacius from his bishopric.

It was the state, then, that initiated the use of force against heresy. In 438 the emperor Theodosius II says, "The first duty of the imperial majesty is to protect the true religion, whose worship is intimately connected with the prosperity of human undertakings." Thus, the civil power persecuted the Manichaean heresy by confiscation and exile. The sentence of death was also used, though the number of such executions was not great. The Church remained opposed to the use of force. Even in the twelfth century St. Bernard could say, "Faith is a matter of persuasion, not of force."

The *Declaration on Religious Freedom* issued by the

Second Vatican Council, promulgated on December 7, 1965, definitively states the Church's attitude toward religious freedom and all use of force.

This Vatican Council declares that the human person has a right to religious freedom. This freedom means that all men are to be immune from coercion on the part of individuals or of social groups and of any human power, in such wise that no one is to be forced to act in a manner contrary to his own beliefs, whether privately or publicly, whether alone or in association with others, within due limits. This council further declares that the right to religious freedom has its foundation in the very dignity of the human person as this dignity is known through the revealed word of God and by reason itself. This right of the human person to religious freedom is to be recognized in the constitutional law whereby society is governed and thus it is to become a civil right."

Further on in the Declaration there is a recognition that in times past this right of man to religious freedom has been violated. The terms in which this statement is put are general, since many historical forces were at work in any period of persecution. Yet it is clear that the Declaration intends to admit humbly that the People of God have not always been true to their Christian ideal.

"In faithfulness therefore to the truth of the Gospel, the Church is following the way of Christ and the apostles when she recognizes and gives support to the principle of religious freedom as befitting the dignity of man and as being in accord with divine revelation. Throughout the ages the Church has kept safe and handed on the doctrine received from the Master and from the apostles. In the life of the People of God, as it has made its pilgrim way through the vicissitudes of human history, there has at times appeared a way of acting that was hardly in accord with the spirit of the Gospel or even opposed to it. Nevertheless the doctrine of the Church that no one is to be coerced into faith has always stood firm.

"Thus the leaven of the Gospel has long been about its quiet work in the minds of men, and to it is due in great measure the fact that in the course of time men have come more widely to recognize their dignity as persons, and the conviction has grown stronger that the person in society is to be kept free from all manner of coercion in matters religious."

The cruel violence of the Inquisition, then, cannot claim a foundation in the doctrine of the Catholic Church. It has been a matter of embarrassment and regret that this institution ever came into existence and received support even from popes.

2

When the Albigensian heresy first entered France early in the eleventh century its adherents deeply offended the simple faith of the simple people. There are several cases of mob violence on record, heretics being seized by the people and put to death, all in the name of the good Christ! After several years of sporadic lynchings of heretics (in which the Church had no hand whatsoever) it seems that the members of this sect began their quiet boring from within. Outwardly they appeared to be good Catholics, attending religious services and living a life undistinguishable from their neighbors. Secretly, however, they practiced their Albigensian religion and strove to spread it as valiantly as any missionary. In 1140 there were signs that the heresy was making strong inroads into southern Germany and the Netherlands. The religious leaders in the area were totally incapable of dealing with it. They asked the foremost preacher of the day to come to their assistance. Thus it was that St. Bernard of Clairvaux once more left his monastery to lend his wisdom and his eloquence to the fight.

Bernard was a remarkable man, full of paradoxes. He was born in 1091 into a well-to-do family. While still young he felt the need of devoting himself entirely to the service of God and the Church. He chose a new and very strict order which had established its first monastery at Citeaux near his home. This was, of course, the Cistercians, a group of monks devoted to a life of contemplation and withdrawal from the world. Bernard was soon made abbot of a new foundation in

Clairvaux, whose name he has taken into history with his own. He could not remain sequestered in his monastery, however, as great as was his love of solitude. His writings and his sermons were too powerful and too full of learning to pass unnoticed. He was called to trouble spots throughout Europe. He was involved in almost every ecclesiastical and secular dispute that occurred during his lifetime. His famous debate with Abelard is well known. Bernard was the preacher selected by the pope to call together the armies for the second crusade. By his efforts the Cistercians shortly became the most influential order of its times. In 1145 a Cistercian monk who had begun his monastic life at Clairvaux became Pope Eugenius III, and thus the great contemplative became an adviser of popes. Yet it is true that Bernard was never happier than when in his monastery, and it was there that he fled as soon as each piece of business was finished. It was there that he died in 1153, surrounded only by his monks.

St. Bernard had no notable success in his first tilt with the Albigenses in the valley of the Rhine. Though he re-converted some, the main body of heretics was intact upon his departure. This new aberration was difficult to understand and its adherents were too slippery to be netted in the fine web of reason and argument. When Eugenius III became pope in 1145 he received an urgent alarm from his legate Alberic in southern France that the entire area was honeycombed with heresy. The new pope thought at once of his spiritual father and instructed Alberic to seek the aid of Bernard. The abbot of Clairvaux left his monastery once again and hastened to Languedoc. He immediately recognized that his foe was the same as in Germany, the heresy of the Albigenses. Here it was widespread, and at time almost open. Besides, other false teachers were abroad in the land, including Henry, the Monk of Lausanne, whose teachings were mainly anti-clerical. The chroniclers of Bernard's life recount that his success in Southern France was immense and that churches could not hold the crowds that came to hear him preach. A closer examination of the history of the region shows us that the heresy continued to be rampant in the towns of Toulouse, Albi, and Narbonne for another two centuries. Bernard had little effect on the basic situation in the area. He did place a number of monasteries under obedience to Clairvaux and sent his own monks to staff them. He hoped to remove the scandal of worldly monks and edify the people by the ascetic life of the Cistercians. Later, the Cistercians furnished from their monasteries the first inquisitors.

The Church tried another tactic to rid Languedoc of heresy, and the result was a series of wars lasting for twenty-five years during the first part of the twelfth century. This was the Albigensian Crusade, launched against the counts of Toulouse who refused to persecute and wipe out the heretics. Count Raymond VII was a Catholic himself, but so many of his nobles and churchmen were Albigensians that he hesitated to move aaginst them for fear of undermining authority throughout the territory. Besides, he was too involved in wars and negotiations with the French king to risk dividing his people. Pope Innocent III declared that he was unworthy to rule and freed all his vassals from allegiance to him. The lands could be captured by any Catholic with an army strong enough to take them. The story of these wars, with shifting tides of battle, are too confusing and peripheral to recount here. Suffice it to say that after twenty-five years of fighting, and the best efforts of even Simon de Montfort, the count of Toulouse was still firmly entrenched in his territory and the heretics were stronger than ever.

3

The Church was not without its weapons against heresy, and the means of discovering it and conquering it were always at hand. The reason for its persistence and its spread rested squarely on corruption within the Church itself. Pope Innocent III correctly diagnosed the state of affairs when he said, "The corruption of the people has its chief source in the clergy. From this corruption arises the evils of Christendom: Faith perishes, religion is defaced, liberty is restricted, justice is trodden underfoot, the heretics multiply, the schismatics are emboldened, the faithless grow strong." If bishops had been truly religious men the lower clergy would have been more exemplary and the laity more true to their baptismal promises. But the bishops were men of power and wealth, more concerned with temporal affairs than secular, more often put into power by families eager to have access to the wealth and influence of the Church. Bishops often did not live in their dioceses, and less seldom visited the parishes or met the people. The shepherds did not watch over the flock, and it is no wonder that the sheep wandered.

In the tenth century bishops were directed to visit each parish in their diocese once a year. While living at the parish he selected seven men of good reputation, known as *synodal witnesses,* who were sworn to reveal what they knew, or what they learned thereafter about any injustices or wrong-doing in the parish. This direction was repeatedly given to bishops over the next two centuries. Pope Lucius III directed all bishops to make the yearly visitation and to swear two men to reveal whatever they knew about heresy. The Emperor Frederick Barbarossa, in 1184, directed all local rulers to swear that they would aid the Church in discovering heresy. This system of visitations could have uncovered heresy while it was still in its infancy, and the Church had ample means to apply spiritual poultices to this lesion in its body. It was not used, and heresy spread until it became a danger to both Church and state.

Also in the tenth century there was a revival of the study

of Roman Law, with a consequent interest in revising and codifying canon law, those regulations by which the Church is governed. The new canon law provided for three ways of taking action against violators. First was the *accusatio*. In this case an individual made an accusation against another, and his charge was investigated. The person making the accusation was subject to the old law of retaliation if his allegation was proved false. In that case, he suffered the same penalty that the one he accused would have suffered. The second form was the *denunciatio*. This was the accusation of a public official whose duty it was to bring offenses to the attention of authorities. The revelations of the synodal witnesses mentioned above fell into this category. The third form was the *inquisitio*. In this method of proceeding against suspects the bishop notified the accused that he was under investigation. The suspected man was brought before the bishop or his delegate, where he heard the charges against him read. He was then questioned. If he confessed or convicted himself, the matter proceeded immediately for punishment. Otherwise, witnesses were called to give evidence. If the bishop thought necessary, the suspect might be imprisoned while the investigation was underway. There were at this time ecclesiastical prisons, and it was in one of these that the accused was kept if he was confined. At the end of the *inquisitio* the bishop pronounced his verdict. If the bishop was uncertain even yet, he could require *purgation* of the accused. In purgation a number of men, peers of the accused, came forward to testify that they deemed the suspected man innocent. In so doing, they made themselves liable to punishment should the man later be found guilty indeed. This third way was the one that developed into the Inquisition.

Just how much good could be accomplished under systems in existence before the establishment of the Inquisition is seen the case of Bishop Foulques of Toulouse. This energetic and worthy bishop of a city ridden with Albigensianism brought about the Council of Toulouse in 1229, just as the Albigensian Crusades were ending in frustration. In attendance at this council were the archbishops, bishops, and abbots, as well as the leading barons and the papal legate, Romano. Not contenting himself with a council that passed a few futile regulations, he brought it about that the entire body became a court of inquisition. A converted Albigensian was found who was willing to give evidence against his former fellows. In short order there were so many witnesses that each of the bishops was kept busy taking evidence. All the information was gathered together and presented to the legate Romano, who took the documents with him when he hastened away to another local council. Heretics who suspected that incriminating evidence had been presented against them followed the legate and asked him to show them the list of witnesses who had testified against them. Romano knew that the men had the right to know their accusers, but he feared that informers might be killed if their names became known. He compromised by showing the petitioners the entire list of witnesses without specifying who had testified against whom. Even so, several murders were committed in Toulouse because of this investigation. Romano examined the cases carefully and imposed sentences on flagrant heretics. He sent these back to Bishop Foulques who summoned all the accused to the cathedral and there read out the sentences. This case illustrates clearly that bishops who were truly concerned with the state of their dioceses had ample means to guard their flock, even if it meant hard and frustrating work.

It is not easy to assign one particular date as the beginning of the Inquisition. Some have placed the beginning at April 20, 1233, when Pope Gregory IX appointed the Dominicans to seek out heretics. Some place the date as May 15, 1252, when Pope Innocent IV issued his bull, *Ad Extirpanda*. It seems that the institution developed gradually, each event strengthening the structure previously erected. Perhaps we might say that the Inquisition was inevitable once the feudal system was established and the roles of Church and state became confused. When heresy became a political crime as well as a religious error it was certain that religious unorthodoxy would be sought out and persecuted.

In the thirteenth century several laws were placed on the books making heresy illegal. Even before this time, however, most rulers already treated heresy as treason against themselves. In 1220 the Holy Roman Emperor Frederick II made all towns and provinces place in the legal code laws that declared heretics to be criminals. The property of a convicted heretic was confiscated and his children disinherited. Neither his children nor his grandchildren could hold any civil or ecclesiastical office. Houses of heretics were burned, and were not to be rebuilt. (This latter regulation had to be mitigated, since eventually the amount of bare land in cities became uneconomical.) Pope Honorius III also ordered that these edicts of Frederick be incorporated into the laws of the towns. He further ordered that schools of law teach and comment on these regulations. Though Frederick's laws applied only to the Holy Roman Empire, which consisted of Germany and parts of Italy, other rulers soon adopted the same policy. In 1229 an edict was issued in the name of Louis IX of France, then only a child, enforcing the same regulations in that kingdom. In 1234 Count Raymond of Toulouse somewhat unwillingly accepted all points of Frederick's legislation. Thus, before the Inquisition was established, the civil law already had a complete code of persecution.

Obviously, the state could not determine the presence of heresy itself. It was for the Church to declare who was unorthodox in matters of faith. According to the organization of the Church, this obligation rested upon the bishop, who had complete jurisdiction within his diocese. The papal Inquisition developed when bishops did not do their duty within their own territories. One case which led to papal intervention occurred in 1227, when the bishop of Florence was himself an Albigensian. Since the diocese could not act in this case, Pope Gregory IX himself set up a commission to look into the case. The bishop, Filippe Paternon, was placed in prison while the commission, consisting of two Dominicans and a canon of the cathedral, conducted their investigation. Friends of the bishop, however, rescued him. Paternon fled from the city and all trace of him was lost. The importance of this case is that the pope invaded the jurisdiction of Florence. It was quite proper that he should do so, but it set a precedent for prosecution of heresy belonging directly to Rome.

On April 20, 1233, Pope Gregory IX issued two bulls, one addressed to the bishops, the other to the Order of Preachers, the Dominicans. This was a significant action, for it laid the groundwork for the papal inquisition, with the inquisitors being responsible only to the pope. These bulls, or decrees issued under the pope's seal (bulla), did not take the seeking out of heresy from the jurisdiction of the bishops, but asked them to accept the help of the Dominicans. "We," the bull to the bishops read, "seeing that you are in the midst of a whirlwind of cares and hardly able to breathe in the pressure of overwhelming anxieties, judge it well to divide your burdens that they may be more easily borne. We have therefore decided to send preaching friars against the heretics of France and the neighboring provinces, and we beg, warn, and exhort you, ordering you as you reverence the Holy See, to receive them kindly and give them good treatment. We ask you to give them favor, counsel, and the aid they need to fulfill their office." The letter addressed to the Dominicans enpowers all Dominicans to act as papal legates in the matter of seeking out and punishing heretics, giving them the power to act without appeal.

The traditional orders of the Church, the Benedictines and the Cistercians, had failed to perform well as preachers against heresy and seekers after it. First of all, these were monastic orders, and the members did not have the mobility or freedom requisite for their task. Second, these orders at this time were marked by worldliness, a trait scarcely able to command respect or call for adherence to the Church. There were two new orders within the Church that met the needs of the times and whose members were held in high respect by all because of their exemplary lives. These were the Dominican priests who were active in the preaching against the Albigensians. The Franciscans, or Friars Minor, were founded in 1209 by St. Francis of Assisi. Both of these orders had the mobility necessary for the work of prosecuting heresy, and a vitality that made them particularly apt instruments. From this time we find the work of the Inquisition entrusted to the members of these two orders.

The Inquisition was now fairly under way, operating on the principles laid down in both ecclesiastical and civil law. For about fifteen years the Dominicans and Franciscans diligently searched out heresy in the fertile fields of northern Italy and southern France. Those convicted were given sentences of various severity. There was conflict, however, between the Inquistors and the bishops, for the lines of authority were far from clear. The bishops naturally resented an invasion of their jurisdiction and often protested violently to the pope. In most cases the pope ruled in favor of the bishops, for the idea of overruling their authority was too novel to gain ready acceptance. Yet, the new inquisitors were effective, much more so than the old diocesan inquisitions. It was only a matter of time until the Inquisition was established on an independent basis.

On May 15, 1252, Pope Innocent IV issued his bull *Ad Extirpanda*. This was addressed to the rulers of Italy only, but in short order its effectiveness was extended to all parts of Europe and became the customary practice. According to this bull, anyone could seize a heretic and confiscate his goods. In each territory there were to be two inquisitors chosen from the Franciscans and the Dominicans. Each ruler was to appoint twelve men, to be assisted by two notaries and at least two servants or guards, whose sole duty was to seize heretics and bring them before the inquisitors. The salary and the expenses of these men was to be paid by the state. The ruler was bound to come to the aid of the Inquisition when called upon, furnishing armed men and money. The bull further decreed that all parts of the edict were to be incorporated into civil law. Torture was provided for in this edict, and the rulers were ordered to apply the torture to those who did not confess. This remarkable document, once accepted by local councils of bishops throughout Europe, served as the charter of the Inquisition.

Apparently it never occurred to anyone that the rights of the heretics were violated by this persecution. The measures were taken to insure survival of both Church and state. Of course, the best way for the Church to stamp out heresy was for it to reform itself, but this again never seemed to be considered. The losing battle of the Inquisition was fought for two hundred years, until Luther's revolt forced the Church to reform itself at the Council of Trent.

Harvesting Wheat in the 16th Century.

Pope Innocent III (1198-1216), Issues Bull Against Heretics.

3

The Inquisition at Work

1

SUPPOSE THAT YOU ARE a villager of Avignonet about the year 1200. Your world is very small. The big town of Toulouse, with its ten thousand citizens, is only thirty-five miles away, but you may not go there once during your life. You know that Count Raymond his his castle there, and you hear rumors of the many battles he has with the French king who wishes to add this territory of Languedoc to his lands. These big affairs, however, are remote to you, for your life is bound up with the life of the village. The Benedictine abbey of Avignonet dominates your life and the abbot is your lord. You have a small plot of land which you and your wife and your children farm, and from it you manage to scrape a meager existence. Your usual meals are bread and vegetables, and perhaps on big feast days you might have a chicken, a rabbit, or even a piece of beef. Besides working your own land, which you hold from the Lord Abbot, you are obliged to work the lord's lands almost a third of the year. On most days life is drab, work beginning at sun-up and ending at sundown. Sundays, however, are good days, for then you go with your family and neighbors to the abbey church. There is the colorful ceremony of the Mass and, if you are fortunate, a good, long sermon, though these sermons are preached rarely enough. After Mass you spend the rest of the morning in the courtyard outside the church talking and gossiping with your fellow-worshippers. Feast days were days to remember. The church ceremonies were of greater-than-usual splendor, and there were games and contests afterwards. Perhaps there might even be a procession. Sometimes the Lord Abbot had to furnish men for the armies of Count Raymond, and you saw the feverish preparations for departure of the small band of soldiers, or perhaps you went yourself. Occasional travelers on the way to Toulouse or Carcassonne passed through Avignonet and you examined their dress and listened to the tales they told about the far away outside world. Mostly, however, your life is dull, a simple struggle for mere existence.

Then, one Sunday, everything changes. At Mass a monk tells the people that the inquisitor from Toulouse is to visit Avignonet. The conversation afterwards in the courtyard is strained. No one talks about the impending visit. A moment of diversion is furnished later in the week by the arrival of the party of the inquisitor. Down the road come a band of men on horses, spirited beasts such as the abbot rides. Some of them carry arms, and others seem to have the stoop of scholars. In the rear rides a lone Franciscan friar on a donkey, for the sons of St. Francis never rode horses. This friar, you hear, is the famous Bernard Delicieux, one of the inquisitors of Toulouse. Since Avignonet is such a small town only one inquisitor comes, along with two notaries, six secretaries, and a band of ten armed men to carry out the commands of the inquisitor. It is a noble sight. Children run alongside to gawk at the men; women run to the doors to stare: the men in the fields look up from their work to see the little parade turn into the grounds of the monastery. Suddenly, the air seems chill upon the village of Avignonet.

The next Sunday the Mass is celebrated with special solemnity. A platform is built right in the middle of the Church. After Mass, the Franciscan inquisitor Bernard ascends the steps. He is a lean man, his eyes deep-sunk, yet seeming to burn with unguessed fires. Standing there, he is the symbol of all that is fearful and terrible about religion, bespeaking impossible renunciations and frightening penances. You know, looking at him, that his God is a God to be feared. He begins to speak, taking as his text the words "My just man lives by faith." The faith, his harsh and strident voice shouts, is the entire faith entrusted to the Church. That is the faith that the just man lives by. One who lives by any other faith is a traitor deserving of punishment. Yet (and here his voice rises to thunder) there are those who dare to hold beliefs other than those handed down by Christ to his apostles and their successors. This is intolerable, and in mercy to their souls he has come to bring them to penance and enlightenment. All men of this parish are commanded to help the inquisitor in his just and merciful work.

"If you know aught of any heresy, any false and pernicious doctrine, held or taught by any within this town, I command you to come forward and tell me within the next ten days. Even if it is your wife, or your child, whom you suspect, you must let me know. Even if it is only the slightest suspicion you must come forward and let me and my associates judge whether there is any truth in the suspicion. If you do not come forward, I warn you that you are thereby punished by excommunication. In his kindness, the Holy Father has authorized me to reward your good intentions by granting an indulgence to those who come to give evidence during this period. Now, to those who know themselves to be heretics, those who gather together secretly to worship in infamous ways, I give a message of mercy. If you come forward of your own accord within the next fifteen days, showing yourself penitent and willing to abjure your errors, you will be treated with mercy and understanding. Should you neglect to take advantage of this period of mercy, then know that you will be hunted and taken, as the hound harries the rabbit. Then, perhaps, you will not find us so merciful."

There are few conversations in the courtyard this Sunday morning. After hurried greetings each family seems to scurry to the safety of home. With a heavy heart and a sense of foreboding you too hasten to your small house. A faithful Christian, you do not worry about the necessity of condemning yourself to the inquisitor. All the same, you have worries. You have seen many comings and goings at the house of Pierre, the weaver. In a village like Avignonet this is strange. Is Pierre one of the dread Albigenses? Do they hold their meetings in his house? And what of Claude, your fellow-farmer, who always speaks so strongly against the priests and bishops? Must you denounce him? You think of Arnaud who seems to hate you so much. Will he satisfy his hatred by denouncing you as a heretic? What if one of your neighbors thinks he might obtain your land or your possessions if you should be taken by Inquisition? Really, they couldn't prove anything, but then, if one of your friends should prove a heretic, that in itself would make you suspect. You glance at your wife, calmly preparing dinner. She wouldn't want to be rid of you, would she? You think of all the other houses in Avignonet, and you know that in each one men and women are thinking similar thoughts. What will all this worry lead to? Will some cracked mind wreak havoc on many lives? What to do—go forward with your suspicions that are not really suspicions, or sit tight? What to do—indulge your envies and spites, or hold your peace and hope your enemies do likewise? A week of torture has begun.

This little vignette shows the evil forces unleashed upon any community by the coming of the Inquisition to its boundaries. It nourished distrust of neighbors and broke the bonds of many friendships. No one, even the innocent, knew whether or not he would be denounced. Grudges and hatreds found ample means of satiation. What little happiness there was in the hard life of the towns and villages vanished under the all-pervading fog of fear. The case of Accursio Aldebandini in the mid-thirteenth century illustrates well the fear the Inquisition could inspire in even the innocent. Aldebrandini was a rich merchant of Florence who traveled much in the course of his business. While stopping in Paris he met a small group of friendly and personable men with whom he spent time in conversation. Later, meeting them on the street, he politely bowed to them. An acquaintance told Aldebrandini one day that his friends had been taken by the Inquisition and accused of heresy. The merchant was in terror. If anyone had seen him bowing to his friends he was in danger, for bowing could be interpreted as the reverence the Albigenses paid to the "perfected." Should the Inquisition hear about him it was unlikely that he would escape without sentence. Aldebrandini was rich enough and important enough to go to Rome immediately and gain a hearing from Pope Gregory IX. He explained his case to the pope, who heard him sympathetically but nevertheless appointed a commission of two bishops to look into his orthodoxy. After examining him closely, the bishops reported that the merchant was beyond suspicion. Thereupon the Pope wrote to the Inquisition in Paris, instructing them to take no action against Aldebrandini. This man was fortunate enough to have anticipated his plight, and rich enough to seek an avenue of escape. What of those who were not so lucky?

There are several cases we know of in which false witness was brought against innocent men. The case of Pons Arnaud of Languedoc, in 1312, is an illustration. Pons came forward during the time when the inquisitors were seeking information and accused his own son, Pierre. Pons claimed that he had been very sick, so much so that his family was sure he would die. It was during this time, Pons said, that Pierre came to him and tried to have him hereticated into the Albigensian heresy. The father recovered, however, and now came forward to accuse his son. When the son vehemently denied the charge, the inquisitors investigated and found that Pons had not been sick at all during the period he had indicated, nor, according to the information of the inquisitors, had there been heretics in that town at that time. Faced with this evidence the father confessed that he and his son were on bad terms, and that he had attempted to ruin him by a false accusation. The inquisitors ordered him to wear two pieces of red cloth, shaped like tongues, on his back and breast for the rest of his life, a sign that he was a perjurer. It is good to note that false witnesses were sometimes tripped up, but we cannot help wondering how many succeeded in making their spite charges stick.

What penalties could the inquisition inflict? If a person refused to renounce his heresy, or relapsed into heresy after conversion, he could be turned over to the "secular arm" for execution by burning at the stake. Even if the heretic repented he could receive a severe penalty of imprisonment, usually for life. (When we examine the case of St. Joan of Arc in the next chapter we will see that this was the first sentence imposed upon her. She was later burned as a relapsed heretic.) Next in severity was banishment, sometimes to the Holy Land. The inquisitor could ask the convicted to make a series of pilgrimages, either to several local shrines, or such difficult and lengthy pilgrimages as to St. James of Compostella in Spain, to Rome, or to the Holy Land. Such pilgrimages were extremely lengthy and dangerous, as well as expensive. Often the pilgrim did not return. One of the lightest sentences was also one of the most burdensome. A convicted heretic, upon repentance, could be condemned to wear crosses of yellow cloth upon his back and breast, proclaiming to all who saw him that he had been a heretic. This punishment was for a period of time, or even for life. Wearers of the yellow crosses were held up to ridicule everywhere, the butt of children's mocking, the scorn of people, persecuted wherever they went. The crosses were the ruination of merchants, a condemnation to the single state for the unmarried. There are cases on record of young women permitted to take off their crosses to enable them to find a husband.

A peculiar custom of the Inquisition was to try even the dead. If convicted, their bodies were exhumed and burned at the stake. The reason for this was partly economic. The children of a heretic, or descendants to the third degree, could not inherit, nor hold public office. When a dead man was convicted it was the children who were the real victims.

How often were these severe penalties inflicted? There is no complete record of the sentences of the Inquisition, so no figures can be given that have any accuracy. Sometimes critics of the Inquisition give horrifying figures of burnings by the tens of thousands. While the situation was bad enough, it was hardly that bad. We do have a record of one inquisitor's sentences covering a fifteen year period. During that time he passed sentence on 636 persons. Here is a list of some of these:

burned	40	condemned to	
bodies exhumed		wear crosses	138
and burned	67	pilgrimages	16
imprisoned	300	banished to the	
fugitives	36	Holy Land	1

A word should be said about burning at the stake. This horrible death was first inflicted upon heretics by the Roman emperors, and remained thereafter as a punishment favored by vigilante mobs. The Church, quite properly, claimed a horror of inflicting death. It is sad to relate that churchmen, forgetting that they represented the Savior who would not cast the first stone, used legalistic formulas to condemn men to the stake while escaping the seeming responsibility for the act. The Church through the inquisitors, never pronounced a sentence of death. Instead, it "relaxed the prisoner to the secular arm," or "withdrew the protection of the Church." Thus, the civil officials inflicted the actual punishment while ministers of the Church stood by to grant absolution should the condemned ask it at the last moment. Yet this was mere subterfuge, for it was the Church which demanded that the secular powers seek out heresy and punish it by death. The local officials were sworn to carry out the sentences of the Inquisition. Catholics have too often tried to explain away these executions, always without being convincing. The Second Vatican Council tried no such polemics, but admitted, as we have seen, that the pilgrim Church has sometimes acted in a manner quite contrary to the teachings of her Founder. Catholics wiser than those who try to rationalize these executions point out that the Church's official teaching never countenanced what some bishops and even popes did. They say that the Church's claims are bolstered by the fact she survived these abuses which would have been enough to destroy any man-made institution. Though men erred, as men will, the institution of the Church itself went on to purify itself and continue its pilgrim march, teaching other men a gentler way of life. The sins of the Inquisition were mainly the prevailing sins of the times.

3

Imagine once again that you are a villager of Avignonet. Thirty days have now passed since the inquisitor arrived in the village. The period of grace is over. You have noticed your neighbors slipping into the monastery grounds, and you grimly tell yourself that someone will suffer in Avignonet. The tension in the village is now nigh unbearable. Some zealots are anxious to see any heretics punished, and some have consciences so pure that they have no fear for themselves. You are not overly worried, for you consider yourself a good Christian. Your only fear is that you may be falsely denounced by some unknown enemy, or that chance remarks or actions of yours might be misinterpreted.

You are surprised, therefore, and somewhat alarmed, though not overcome, when two bailiffs of the inquisition approach you in the field.

"Come with us," they say. "The Inquisitor wishes to speak with you."

"Eh? Well, as soon as I tell my wife," you say.

"No. Come at once. Your wife will know."

You wonder as you trudge across the fields what the Inquisitor wishes from you. Perhaps he wants to ask you about some neighbors. Perhaps he is seeing everyone in the village. You hardly dare think that you are under suspicion. You follow the bailiffs among the outbuildings of the monastery and come to the cottage being used by the Inquisitor. On entering, you see the Inquisitor seated behind a desk. With him are two secretaries, their pens poised above sheets of parchment. Two witnesses are seated at the side of the room, and a notary sits on the other side. You enter with confidence, for you find your conscience clear.

(This interrogation is based upon a model drawn up by one of the most famous inquisitors, Bernard Gui, for the instruction of other inquisitors.)

"Why have you been brought here?"

The voice of the Inquisitor is soft and gentle, seeming to smooth away cares and fears.

"Sir, I thought you asked for me. Surely you will tell me the reason," you reply.

"You have been accused as a heretic, as one who believes and teaches contrary to that which the Church teaches."

The voice of the Inquisitor is still mild, his face still gentle, his whole demeanor inviting confidence. For your part, you are thunderstruck. The room seems to reel before your eyes as your heart fills with despair.

"No!" you cry. "This is not so. I have always been a good Christian."

"You call yourself a good Christian, for you consider our Christianity false," replies the Inquisitor, and now a hint of steel enters his voice. The smile is gone from his lips. There is silence for a moment, the only sound being the pens tracing letters upon the parchment. The case against you is being built up!

"I ask you whether you have ever believed as true another faith than that which the Roman Church holds to be true," the Inquisitor asks.

"I believe the true faith which the Roman Church believes, and which you openly preach to us," you reply.

"Ah. Perhaps some of your sect at Rome call themselves the Roman Church. And I, when I preach, say many things that both of us believe, such as that God lives. But you may be a heretic in not believing other matters."

"I believe all things that a Christian should believe."

"I know your tricks," thunders the Inquisitor. "What the members of your sect believe, that is what you say a Christian should believe."

"Sir, I beg you, tell me who charged me, and perhaps I can defend myself better."

"No, I can tell you no names. You have the right to give the names of any who might have a mortal enmity toward you, and if your accuser is among them, we will take that into consideration. Do you have any such names to give us?"

You cudgel your memory for any you have insulted, and any who might have reason to resent you. Really, you can't think of any who have a mortal enmity toward you, but obviously there is one such. After much thought you put forward some names.

"There is Pierre the farmer, who thought I stole some of his wheat, but I didn't. And there is Francois the shoemaker, who always seems to have sour looks for me."

The Inquisitor glances down to his paper, then looks up slowly.

"No, those names are not here. So you see, no enemy has accused you, but one who loves the Church and wants the salvation of your soul."

"Sir, I do not know what to say. I can only repeat that I am entirely innocent. If there are charges against me, perhaps I can refute them."

"Did you not say," the Inquisitor asks, looking down at a sheet of paper, "that you never saw a heretic riding a horse as sleek and fat as the mounts used by the monks?"

You pale, for you recall making that remark while walking home after Mass one Sunday. Who was about then, you cannot recall. It seemed innocent enough then, for Father Abbot did indeed ride a horse that a count would be proud to own. It seemed unfitting to you then, and even as you stand here accused, it still seems unfitting. Yet it is a wisp of suspicion, and you do not know what to say.

"And did you not remark that you had scarce seen Mass celebrated by a skinny man?"

"Sir," you stammer, "these mean nothing. They are but my unworthy complaints about my own ill fortune. I have no vow of poverty, but I live poorly indeed."

"Ah," the Inquisitor exclaims dryly. "You would not

mean to say, would you, that the Mass and sacraments are nothing but shams in the hands of an unworthy priest?"

"I do not know what you mean, sir."

"No. Of course. You would not know, would you, that your friends, the Albigenses, teach such things? But tell me, do you know Charles, the son of Pierre, he who is called 'the Wise'?"

"Yes, sir, I know him well," you reply, for indeed you do. You know everyone in the small village of Avignonet, but you have had a special fondness for old Charles. He is the village philosopher. In his little spare time he often sat outside his hut, carving a piece of wood into a small statue of the Christ-Child, or a likeness of a farmer, or sometimes just carving a toy whistle for a child. You often visited him, and listened to him talk as the chips of wood fell about his stool. Sometimes he spoke of times long ago, of people now lying in peace on the hill beyond the village. Other times he commented on what was happening this small world you shared with him, and you listened as he explained the principles by which he lived, and commented on why people did the things they did. He was immensely interesting and always wise.

"Your friend Charles is a heretic," the Inquisitor says. "He has confessed that he is a perfected Albigensian. Did you see him often?"

You stand pale and trembling, for though you know yourself innocent, you can see that the wisp of suspicion has grown into a fog, the thread into a web. Further, you are stunned by the news of old Charles.

"I see you are silent," remarks the Inquisitor. Then, to the guards, "Very well, let him meditate for a while on bread and water. Take him to a cell."

As you are led away and taken to a prison cell, a notary arises to address the Inquisitor.

"Certainly there is reason for suspicion, sir, but there was nothing solid against that man. Everything he did can have an innocent explanation. Who, for instance, has not complained against the lives of some priests and bishops? As for his friendship with a heretic, well, sir, you know what an engaging rascal the old man was. He must be an interesting man to listen to."

"Slippery," said the Inquisitor succinctly. "Did you notice how he avoided my questions at the beginning?"

"He is only an ignorant peasant, sir. He can easily be tripped up in his words, for he has no learning. His evasions can be put down to his inability to express himself."

"You said there was reason for suspicion," commented the Inquisitor. "That in itself is a crime. The just man is above suspicion."

Indeed, the Inquisitor was right. Since cases often could not be proved absolutely, suspicion itself became a crime. There were three degrees, the learned lawyers said. Light suspicion, usually brought on by a single accusation, could be purged by having from three to twenty of the accused's peers swear with him that he was innocent. The second degree of suspicion was "vehement," the third, "violent." A person under vehement suspicion could suffer imprisonment for as long as life, and one under violent suspicion might even die at the stake unless he confessed and showed himself penitent. In your case, now under suspicion, what began as light suspicion has now developed into vehement suspicion because of your relationship with Charles.

Meanwhile, you have been taken into another building of the monastery. The guards half lead, half drag you down dank steps into a dark, noisome prison area. You pass through a narrow corridor. From behind the doors you hear soft shufflings and low moans. The guards fling open a door and push you in. The door slams shut, and you are in prison. There is the smallest of windows high over your head. The door has a peep-hole, but it can be opened only from the outside. Time passes interminably as you first pace, then lie down upon the mat filled with rushes. You cannot clear your mind of terror. Hours later, it seems, the door is opened by two armed guards. They indifferently give you a mug of water and a slice of hard, course bread. As you eat it, the window overhead grows dark, and soon your first day in prison comes to an end.

Nights and days blur together as you plan your defense, as you rehearse the words you will say when next you are questioned. You do not think that in many villages and cities there are other jails like this, and in each one prisoners are detained. The prison you are in is part of the monastery. In the towns, the rulers of the city must build jails for prisoners of the Inquisition and pay a sum for their maintenance. Most prisoners are condemned to live on bread and water, but the jailers will permit friends and relatives to bring other food. Unfortunately, most people are afraid to visit the prisoners, lest they come under suspicion too. As you suffer in prison you do not realize that your captors judge they are doing you a favor. By providing you with the bread of penance and tears of sorrow, they think they are saving your soul! Every prince and princeling, every duke and count, has his own jails filled with people whom he suspects of plotting against him. In this, the Inquisition is no worse than the secular governments of the time, and indeed, their prisons are more bearable. The sad thing is that the morals of the state rather than the ideals of Christ are followed by those who set themselves up to safeguard the faith.

One day you are roused from your stupor when the key grates in the door at an unaccustomed hour. You stand as a black-robed Benedictine from the monastery enters.

"I have come to give you counsel," he says.

"How long have I been here?"

"Just ten days."

Just ten days! Would it be much longer?

"This is only a small town," the monk says. "The Inquisitor has gone on to another village. He will return to wind up matters here after he has taken evidence in that place. Do you realize your danger?"

"Yes, sir. I know I am in danger of losing my freedom or my life. But I will swear that I am innocent. I am no heretic!"

"If you are, tell me. I will give you absolution for your soul's sake, and intercede for you with the Inquisitor."

"I cannot confess what I have not done. Is there anyone who knows the law who will defend me?"

"No," says the monk, shaking his head. "You must defend yourself. Defending a person accused to the Inquisition is the crime of aiding a heretic."

(The practice of providing lawyers for defense differed from place to place, from time to time. Probably it was more common to see that the accused was represented by a priest who knew both canon and civil law. You are not fortunate enough to be in a territory that follows this practice.)

"When will my case be heard?"

"Tomorrow. Tomorrow the Inquisitor returns. He will hear you tomorrow."

The next day you are led back to the room where the Inquisitor is once more seated among his functionaries. You are weak from your imprisonment, and the light hurts your eyes. Your beard is now unkempt and shaggy.

"Read his statement to him," says the Inquisitor, addressing the secretary.

"I admit that I have praciced heretical atcs," the secretary reads in a dry voice, "and that I have worshipped with those who gathered at the house of Charles, the son of Pierre, a farmer in this village. I admit that I have spoken against the

Church and the clergy. Now I abjure my heresy and beg for your mercy."

For a while all you can do is shake your head over and over again. Finally, you manage to say, "No. No. It is not true. I cannot sign such a statement."

"Very well," says the Inquisitor. "Let the question be put to him."

You know what that statement means. Torture! You are pale and stumbling as the guards almost carry you from the room. They take you to a dungeon room near the prison cells. There you are stripped of your clothes and your hands bound behind your back. The monk who visited you in your cell steps from shadows.

"Will you not confess now? Must the torture be administered?"

"I cannot confess," you say.

Strong hands drag you to a high pole. A rope is fastened to the cords binding your wrist and threaded through an iron ring high over your head. You feel the rope being drawn upward. First your arms rise behind your back, then your whole body is stretched out as you are pulled up onto your toes. Your body rises from the floor — one foot, two, three. You feel the rope grow slack and you plummet down toward the floor, only to stop inches before touching it. Your arms seem pulled from their sockets, your whole body afire. You have just undergone torture by the *strappado*, the most commonly used form of persuasion. The rack and other tortures are spoken of more frequently, but they were rarely used. The *strappado*, skillfully administered, brought exquisite pain without injuring the body. It was often applied for half an hour at a time, the legal limit for torture. (Is it not sad to think that once man tried to apply law to something as lawless as torturing another being?) The Church pretended to abhor this torture, and a priest was present only to order the release of the prisoner if he should confess and to put the question to him from time to time. The torture itself was administered by the secular power. Since the land of your village was owned by the monastery, the bailiff of the monastery was in charge of your torture.

Two, three times more you are hoisted up, and then allowed to fall to that sickening stop. As the ropes tautened for the next pull upward, you cry out.

"Wait. I will confess."

" You are wise," says the monk, signaling to the jailer. "But I must warn you. If you repudiate this confession, it may well be there will be no hope for you. Perhaps then you will be judged a relapsed heretic, and you know that all such are burned at the stake."

"Up! Pull me up'" you shout. "That was weakness. I cannot confess, for I am innocent."

There is a tug at the rope, then a halt as the monk signals again.

"Enough," he says. "Take the prisoner back to his cell."

You are given your clothes and led to your cell once more. The monk comes with you. The Inquisitor will announce his sentences on Sunday he tells you. You will find out your fate then. Until then, he admonishes you to be of good cheer. Good cheer!

While you are awaiting the day of your fate, the Inquisitor calls together his staff, the abbot of the monastery, and some of the learned theologians among the monks. He and his secretaries read each case to this panel of assessors, and propose a sentence for each one. The panel weighs each case, and many questions are asked. Finally, all agree on what sentence should be given in each case.

Meanwhile, preparations are afoot in the monastery and the village. Everyone has been told that on the coming Sunday there will be a "Sermo generalis." This ceremony later came to be called "auto de fe" in Spain. This latter means literally "an act of faith." In its splendor it summed up the power of the entire inquisitorial process. Once again a platform is being erected in the center of the Benedictine church, this time considerably larger than the one built for the Inquisitor alone. In the small village square another platform is being built. More ominously, a fair-sized tree is cut down and trimmed to a height of perhaps ten feet. It is planted in the ground opposite the platform. A quantity of cured wood is piled up near it. Everything is in readiness for the Sunday.

When that Sabbath day dawns you are taken from your cell and brought to a room where you are allowed to wash and groom yourself. Your beard is trimmed and your hair combed. You put on the clean clothes provided. In mid-morning the guards come again to lead you from your cell. You see perhaps twenty of your neighbors and people from outlying dwellings. Old Charles is there. None of you have the spirit to speak to each other. A cross-bearer appears, and you are herded into a line, two by two. Behind you walk the Inquisitor and his retinue. The sad, pitiful procession winds its way through the monastery buildings to the church. The bells have been ringing, summoning the people to worship and to witness the *sermo generalis*. They are assembled in their places as you and the others enter, the women seated upon the right, the men upon the left. You keep your head down in shame as you ascend the steps of the platform and take your place there, raised above your relatives, friends, and neighbors. The procession of monks now enters, and Mass begins. Afterwards, the Inquisitor rises to give the sermon. Again he speaks of the necessity of faith and the evil of heresy. He praises the Inquisition. "The first Inquisition was in the Garden of Paradise," he shouts "It was God Himself who then acted as the first Inquisitor." Then he speaks of the horror that heresy has brought to the village of Avignonet and tells how it has been diligently sought out and discovered. Now is the time when the deeds of each shall be revealed, and just retribution made. The inquisitor calls for the bailiffs and officials of the monastery estate to step forward. He then administers to them an oath by which they swear to uphold and enforce all sentences pronounced by the inquisitorial court. The men do so, and step back. The inquisitor calls out a name and a man stands forward on the platform.

"We have found you innocent of all accusations and you are hereby freed," the inquisitor declares.

Then, your name is called. You step forward, your heart in your mouth. This is the moment feared for so many days.

"We have found you guilty of vehement suspicion of heresy and condemn you to wear upon your back a yellow cross of cloth, and the same upon your breast, these badges of your shame to be worn for a period of one year. You are to attend Mass daily and report to the pastor of the Church each week for instruction. Twice a week shall you fast on bread and water, and thus wash away your guilt."

You are in despair, for how can you now face your friends and neighbors? How will you bear the shame? You have escaped prison, but this punishment seems worse. You feel faint as you step back.

The sentences proceed, one after another, the lighter sentences being announced first. Several others are condemned to wear crosses, two for life. Two are condemned to a year in prison, and one man receives a sentence of being confined in prison for the rest of his life. Finally, there is only the case of old Charles to be announced.

"We find you to be a stubborn and contumacious heretic," the Inquisitor thunders at him, "unrepentant and steadfast in your error. We are therefore obliged to withdraw from you the protection and mercy of the Church, and to release you to the secular arm."

This is the sentence of death. The guards seize the old man and lead him away. Everyone is told to be present in the town square the next day in the early morning. That night, your wife silently cuts the yellow crosses and sews them upon clothes, and as you wear them the first time the shame again rises up within you, and a vast sense of the injustice and wrong. Yet, so strong is the position of the faith in your life, the Church in all your ways of thinking, that you do not even consider blaspheming or railing out against your fate. You do not know how to be anything except a Christian, a loyal son of the Church. You look upon this as an error that must be borne, and indeed, you are thankful to the Inquisitor for having purified the village. It does not occur to you to question the Inquisition.

The next morning you and your neighbors gather in the village square. The abbot and the Inquisitor, along with other important local persons, are assembled on the high platform. Then old Charles appears, led into the square behind a cross-bearer and accompanied by a monk with a crucifix in his hand. Under questioning, Charles again refuses to express repentance. Once more the sentence of release to the secular arm is read, and the old man is led to the stake. The wood is quickly piled about him until he reaches his chin. Shavings are liberally scattered within the wood to make it burn more quickly. The monk remains near the condemned man, holding up his crucifix, but Charles does not seem to heed him. A black-hooded executioner steps forward with a burning brand, applying it to the pyre. The flame rises suddenly, forcing the monk back. There is a cry from the stake, and then silence. Soon the poor man is entirely wrapped in flames. You pray that he is already dead. People begin to leave as soon as the torch is put to the pyre.

The executioner and his aides remain, throwing on new wood until no more than some charred bones remain. These they gather up and throw into the river that winds beyond the town, that no remains and no relics of a supposed martyr may be found. The Inquisitor leaves for the city later in the day, and Avignonet is left purified, with endless days to heal the wounds, the scars, the deep divisions unknown before the Inquisition came to this village.

4

This, in summary form, is how the Inquisition operated. It would be wrong, however, to assume that the Inquisition was everywhere and at all times the same. Oftentimes it was lenient, as much interested in exposing heresy as in punishing it. At other times, in the hands of severe inquisitors, it was unwontedly harsh, and even sadistic. Sometimes all the forms prescribed were not observed in the eagerness to seek out and punish heresy. Some inquisitors operated on the principle that it was better for an innocent man to suffer than for a heretic to go free. Nor was the corruption so common in those times unknown in the Inquisition. Bribes bought both convictions and release. Sometimes inquisitors released the condemned from their condemnation to prison, pilgrimages, or the wearing of crosses upon the offering of a large sum of money, which found its way into the purses of the officials of the Inquisition.

Legalism built up such a web of rules that it became difficult for the innocent to escape. Once a man fell into the net of the Inquisition he was lost beyond recovery. An example of this is the development of suspicion as a crime in itself. Mere babblings of unlearned peasants were twisted by learned theologians into heresy because they lacked theological nicety. The sentences became so formalized that the disposition of the accused had no part in his punishment. The refusal to name the accuser made defense against the charges nigh impossible. When learned legal advice was denied, escape without sentence was highly unlikely.

A disillusioned inquisitor remarked that if St. Peter and St. Paul were brought before the Inquisition and accused of paying homage to heretics, they would not be able to defend themselves. Though they might answer with profound theological insights, the inquisitor would say that nevertheless they had paid homage to heretics. When they asked the names of these heretics, the time, the place, the inquisitor would refuse to supply the information. Thus the legal net encircled the accused while all means of extricating himself were denied him.

Perhaps the greatest weakness of the Inquisition was that it lent itself as a tool of the state for punishing those whose offense was only political. The most famous cases of the Inquisition, those we will examine in the next chapter, were all politically inspired prosecutions, and the doom of the accused was sealed before the inquisitorial process began. As the national states of Europe emerged from the feudal order of the early Middle Ages, rulers took advantage of the blurred lines separating Church and state. When they could not directly destroy an enemy they sought to use the Inquisition to achieve their goal. This proved ever so much more effective than a political execution, for condemnation for heresy destroyed their victim's reputation in the eyes of the people.

The effects of the Inquisition have been long range. Perhaps it is too simplistic to blame the backward economic development of southern Europe upon the Inquisition, yet a case for this charge can be made. Certainly it is one of the factors why Italy and Spain, and to a lesser degree, France, were slower to develop trade and manufacture than Germany and England, where the Inquisition was relatively unknown. Indeed, the Inquisition never reached England, and was only moderately or slightly active in Germany. It was a way of life in Italy, Spain, and southern France for a period of three hundred years. At a time when trade and manufacture were developing in other parts of the world, capital was frightened away from these regions by the laws placed upon the books by the Inquisition. The children, the grandchildren, and the great-grandchildren of a convicted heretic could not inherit, nor could they hold responsible office in either Church or state. A man could be convicted of heresy long after his death, and the disability to inherit applied retroactively to his heirs. The goods of a convicted heretic were confiscated. If he were already dead, his lands and property were taken away from his children. Who would want to lend money to a man whose grandfather could be convicted of heresy, with the result that the man lost all his possessions? Who felt free to engage in any long range activity when at any moment a charge of heresy against a deceased relative might turn him into a pauper? Further, all relationships were poisoned and trust destroyed, for if an associate or borrower were convicted of heresy he brought ruin to all who were connected with him. Capital funds fled to safer lands and men of ability followed them, preferring to live safely in a strange country than to live precariously in their native land. This effect of the Inquisition is often overlooked, but it is important indeed.

A case could be made, too, that the Inquisition impeded the development of humane civil laws. It developed just at the time when the old Roman law was being discovered and finding its way into the legal customs of states. Up to that time, trials by ordeal were common. In such "trials," the accused thrust an arm into boiling water or attempted to walk through fire. If he escaped unharmed, he was proved innocent. Naturally enough, few ever so proved their innocence. So too was torture common. Civilization had reached a point where men were ready to mitigate these barbaric practices, and there were examples of trial by evidence entering the legal codes. Once the use of torture became fixed in the practice of the Inquisition the entire legal code, both ecclesiastical and civil, became corrupted and stunted. It took many long years to resume the development once more.

Worst, of course, was the influence of the Inquisition on the Church itself. The heresies that kept arising were symptoms, not the disease itself. Yet the Church chose to treat the symptoms, using the harshest possible remedies. This of course distracted it from the treatment of the disease, which was difference between the lives of too many Churchmen and the ideal of Christ. Heresies rose up in protest against worldliness. Heresy came about because the masses were neglected by those who should have been their shepherds. Neglected, the common people fell easy prey to preachers of unorthodox doctrines who nevertheless led exemplary lives. The disease was also the intermingling of Church and state so that the Church forgot that the Kingdom of God was not to be equated with any one earthly kingdom, or people, or civilzation. Instead of witnessing to the sufficiency of God, instead of demanding that earthly kingdoms live by godly laws, the Church became a part of the state, aligned herself with the state. These things were the disease, and it was these that had to be treated. Instead, the Church wasted its energies attacking mere symptons, letting precious time slip through the fingers. It was only Luther's revolt that forced the Church to apply healing measures to herself in the Council of Trent. Had the same energy been expended three hundred years earlier, it is likely that when Luther came upon the scene he would not have felt the need to challenge the Church, as several Protestants theologians stated after the Second Vatican Council.

4

Famous Cases of the Inquisition

IN THIS CHAPTER we shall examine very briefly three of the most famous cases of the Inquisition, those of Joan of Arc, John Huss, and Galileo. In none of them is the Inquisition as guilty as commonly supposed. The cases of St. Joan and John Huss are intimately bound up with politics; so much so, it can be said that secular authority simply forced the Inquisition to be its accomplice. The circumstances of these trials illustrate that policies of Gregory VII and Innocent III in the long run injured the Church, for in any confusion of Church and state it is the Church that stands to lose the most. In the case of Galileo we will see that the famous scientist brought most of his troubles upon himself. His difficulties could have easily been avoided, but he persisted in going through all the danger signs. His punishment was not the harsh penalty we might expect, but a comparatively mild sentence that really worked no hardship on him. He was more injured by his loss of reputation than by his confinement, which was in the comfortable quarters of his own home from which he did not travel much in any case.

1

Joan of Arc was born into a peasant family of Domremy on January 6, 1412. She carried her share of the family burden by watching over the family sheep in the pastures outside the town. At the time of her entrance upon stage of world affairs she could neither read nor write. This was not unusual, for education was not often wasted upon women, and illiteracy was not rare among men, even those of high position. As Joan watched over her sheep in the lonely meadows she began to hear voices. She was thirteen when this first occurred. In the beginning they urged her to live a good life. Later, she understood that the voices belonged to St. Michael the Archangel, St. Catherine, and St. Margaret. They began to tell her that she must save France from the English who controlled most of the country. When she was fifteen, the "voices," as she always called them, told her she must raise the siege of Orleans. She must see the king, and then go to the beleaguered city. Her arrival there would bring it deliverance. When she was seventeen, the voices told her that she had hesitated too long, that she must go at once.

The story of how Joan reached the king and secured his support is too well-known to need re-telling. So unusual and portentous was the appearance of the Maid, as the French called her, that her legend began to grow immediately, so that it is difficult to separate the real Joan from legendary details. She was present when the French troops routed the English in front of Orleans. The appearance of a woman in warrior dress so unnerved the English that she immediately became known as a witch. The English leader, Talbot, asserted that he would burn her if he captured her. Joan finally had her desire fulfilled when Charles was crowned in Rheims on July 17, 1429, just five months from Joan's appearance. She stood by in the sanctuary, holding aloft the banner she had carried in her battles. After the coronation of the king

Joan suffered a series of reveses. Ten months later she was captured at the town of Compiegne by Jean de Luxembourg, an ally of the English. He held her for five months until the English paid him a large sum of money which Jean insisted on receiving in cash. He released her, however, only on the condition that she would be tried by the Inquisition. This fitted in well with the plans of the English and they acquiesced.

The town of Compiegne was in the diocese of Beauvais, whose bishop was the infamous Pierre Cauchon. An ardent supporter of the English cause, he was the instrument chosen by the Duke of Bedford, the English commander, to bring about Joan's condemnation. Even while Joan was a captive of Jean de Luxembourg Cauchon had demanded that she be sent to him for trial on the charge of sorcery and errors in the faith. At this time, Cauchon was a fugitive from his own diocese, having been driven out by the people, who were loyal to France. The archbishop of Rouen had died, however, and the seat was vacant. Cauchon obtained permission from the cathedral canons to hold an ecclesiastical trial in Rouen. In other words, he instituted an episcopal inquisition to deal with Joan. The legality of holding a court in another diocese was very doubtful, making it difficult for Cauchon to assemble a panel of assessors whose repute was beyond question. Since the English, however, were determined that Joan must be destroyed and her reputation blackened by the Church, fifty experts in theology and law were assembled. The University of Paris, which supported the cause of the English king, sent several doctors to serve as inquisitorial assessors and examiners.

After her five month imprisonment by Jean, Joan was now brought in chains to Rouen. Since she was now in the hands of the Church she should have been kept in an ecclesiastical prison. The English were not willing to relinquish their prize until she was ready for the stake, and therefore she was kept in the regular jails used for all criminals. She was refused the protection of a matron and the right to hear Mass and receive the sacraments. Joan later protested this violently, but Cauchon could do nothing about this even should he have desired. The English were adamant. The prisoner, they said, must be returned to them even should she be acquitted by the Inquisition.

It was not until February 19, 1431, that Pierre Cauchon felt he was on safe enough legal grounds to proceed. On this date the list of charges against Joan was read to the assessors. The list is long, covering every possible point on which Joan could be convicted. The first charge, of course, was sorcery and dealing with the devil. She was also accused of wearing men's clothes and violating the Apostle Paul's command that women wear long hair. Her "voices" were branded as superstitious and diabolical. With these as the basis of the accusations, the trial began. The assessors and experts refused to proceed with a purely episcopal inquisition and demanded that a representative of the papal Inquisition in France be present. Jean Le Maitre, a Dominican friar, was the inquisitor of Rouen. At first he refused to participate because Cauchon was not in his own diocese, but at length he was persuaded to assist in the trial. Perhaps Le Maitre's hesitancy was due to his knowledge that the English, in any case, would not see Joan go free. With the inquisitor present, Joan was brought before the court for examination. Over a period of three months she was repeatedly summoned for questioning.

Questions were rained upon her by trained theologians, all of them containing a hidden barb. Though Joan was untaught and physically worn down by her months of captivity she skillfully handled these questions. When asked if she was in the state of grace she replied, "If I am not, may the

Lord bring me to it. If I am, may the Lord preserve me in it." Had she answered otherwise, her waiting questioners would have accused her of heresy, using the text, "No man knows whether he is worthy of love or hate." Sometimes her wit flashed out. When asked if St. Michael was naked when he appeared to her, she replied, "Do you not think the Lord of heaven has the wherewithal to clothe his servants?"

At one point the court considered questioning Joan under torture. When she was told that this was a possibility, the Maid replied, "If you torture me, I will confess to anything, but I will deny it later." At length, it was decided not to use torture, primarily because the assessors judged that the case was strong enough without resorting to that extreme. During the questioning the court had found a tricky and sticky point upon which to build a case. When asked if she would renounce the advice of her voices upon the command of the Church, Joan replied that she would submit to God and the saints. Not enough, said her accusers. The Church was established that it might teach and guide men, and men had the duty of giving it obedience in matters spiritual. "Would she submit to the pope?" Joan avoided the question. "Take me to him and I will answer to him." Seeing that Joan was walking a dangerous path the court pressed this line of inquiry relentlessly for days. Finally, Joan affirmed that she would submit to the Church, but only if it did not command what was impossible. "What was impossible?" her accusers wanted to know. She defined as "impossible" whatever went contrary to the commands of the Lord, even those received through her "visions."

This was a difficult point, and remains so to this day. Everyone must act true to his conscience. But then, he also has the obligation of forming his conscience truly. A Catholic holds that the teaching of the Church must be given full weight, for it has the divine command to teach and guide. Any doubtful matter should be decided in favor of the teaching of the Church. Much of the Second Vatican Council's *Declaration on Religious Freedom* deals with this question, and it is no easy one. Speaking on February 2, 1968, Pope Paul VI made a statement on obedience in the Church. "The representatives of Christ," he said, "have pastoral authority and are given the charism of magisterium . . . for the service and salvation of the people of God. The Church is hierarchical, not amorphous. It is not democratic in the sense that no one has priority in matters of faith and doctrine over the one whom the Holy Spirit has placed as the head of the Church of God. This means, in other words, that the Lord has entrusted to some of its members the task of giving to their fellow-members the services of authority and of direction as a principle of unity, of order and of solidarity in effective working together." But, he adds, obedience is to be "responsible, voluntarily given, dutiful, and loving."

Certainly, Joan was incapable of making subtle distinctions and arguing with theological nicety. The church she was talking about was the people she saw before her, whom she recognized as lackeys of the hated English, whom she regularly referred to as the "goddams." Perhaps she could not distinguish in her mind between the human church which she saw judging her, all unjustly, and the divine Church, the "bride of Christ." Even should she have been truly heretical, which she was not, she did not deserve to die for her beliefs. Yet that is what this court had determined upon.

The assessors met on May 19 to consider the evidence and the sentence. There were twelve charges placed against Joan, drawn up in a lengthy document, full of such phrases as, "You savor ill of the faith, you boast vainly, you are suspect of idolatry." All the charges are too lengthy to reproduce here, but among them were: The visions of angels and saints were called superstitious and proceeding from the devil; comparing faith in her visions with faith in Christ was rash and an error in faith; wearing men's clothes and short hair was against biblical commands; reverencing the vision of her "voices" without consulting a priest, which constituted her an idolater; refusing to obey the commands of the Church if contrary to her voices, and rejecting the judgment of the Church. We are horrified today to think that anyone could be put to death on such charges as these. Yet, most of the assessors thought that Joan should be given over to the secular arm without further ado. Some, however, thought that the charges were much too strong. They were not sure that the charges represented Joan's true thinking. She was summoned before the court again on May 23, 1431, where the accusations were read to her one by one. Would she withdraw the statements and the evidence on which each was based? Joan stood firm. There was now the opportunity to send her to the stake.

That day and into the night men were at work building three high platforms in the cemetery of St. Owen alongside the banks of the Seine River. Two were for ecclesiastical and civil dignitaries, while the third was for the court of the inquisition and the prisoner. A stake was erected and wood gathered for the burning.

On the morning of May 24 the court and the people assembled at the cemetery. There was the usual sermon preached, and the charges were once again read. Once more Joan was asked if she would repent and submit. If not, the sentence releasing her to the secular authorities would be pronounced. Seeing the stake before her, and realizing that her death, in such a cruel manner, was a certainty, Joan faltered. She agreed to abjure her statements, and a formula of recantation was read to her. She signed it with an X, for she could not so much as write her name. It should be remembered that Joan was only nineteen years old at this time, full of youth, her memory filled with adventures and moments of high excitement. It is not to be wondered that she shrank from death. She recanted. Then, to her dismay, Pierre Cauchon read the new sentence. She was condemned to perpetual imprisonment on bread and water. Joan cried out, and finally begged that at least she might be kept in an ecclesiastical prison. Cauchon could not order this, for the English would not allow it. She was taken back to the English jail where she had been lodged since the previous October.

As it was, the English were furious. They had no desire to see Joan in prison. They wanted her dead. There was a tense moment as English soldiers drew their swords, threatening Cauchon, Le Maitre, and the other ecclesiastical dignitaries. There was nothing they could do, however, to change the situation, and they led Joan away to her imprisonment. She was at first utterly cowed. Women's clothes were brought to her and she consented to wear them. During her trial she had given as her excuse for wearing men's clothes that she lived among men—rough, fighting men—and that her male attire was a protection to her. In prison she continued to dress like a man since she did not have the protection of an ecclesiastical prison. Now, though her condition had not changed, she put on dresses as did other women. She could not bear the thought of remaining forever in prison, living and dying amid a grey procession of days, with never a soldier's rough but affectionate greeting, with no horn of battle, no bright sun to signal the beginning of a day, no red sunset to soothe the end of it. She repented that she had ever recanted, for death was preferable to this. Besides, had she not betrayed her voices? Had she not denied all she had accomplished? After three days she again put on her soldier's clothes. That they were readily available to her shows that her English jailers had left them in her cell as a temptation and trap. It has even been suggested that her dresses had been taken while she slept, leaving her only the men's clothes she had worn for two years. However it happened, this was interpreted as relapsing into heresy, and now she was doomed beyond recantation. When her judges examined her once again there was a wild scene. Joan claimed she would rather die than remain a prisoner. She had recanted only because of fear, she said, and for this her voices reproached her. The judges had been false to her, for she was still kept in chains, still denied the right to attend Mass and receive the sacraments. Her voices were from God; that, she said, she had never denied. After she had worn herself out with her reproaches she was taken back to prison. The next day, May 29, Cauchon assembled the assessors once again and reported what had occurred. They all agreed that she should be handed over to the English to be burned.

On the next day the *sermo generalis* was held. After the sermon the formula of giving to the secular arm was read, and Joan was bound to the stake. There she was burned, and there here ashes were thrown into the Seine.

Charles, King of France, had not made a single attempt to help the woman who had restored his kingdom. After her death, he felt honor-bound to vindicate her memory, for he could not be indebted to a convicted heretic. He sought from the pope a new investigation so that the verdict of the Inquisition might be overturned. It was finally granted him. In 1456 a papal commission proclaimed that the charges against Joan had been fraudulent and without foundation. Her trial was declared irregular, the whole procedure null and void. To restore her honor, the decree of this commission was ordered read in all cities of the kingdom. It was ordered that a cross be erected on the site of her death, a memorial to a brave woman. Thus was Joan vindicated.

The trial of Joan of Arc, infamous and untypical though it is, illustrates the practice of the Inquisition. It is interesting to note that even in so irregular a procedure as this one was that the rules of the Inquisition provided for mercy to Joan upon her recantation. The purpose of the process was to save the accused if at all possible, and even these unscrupulous men held to the forms and released Joan from condemnation to the stake when she submitted. The sentence to life imprisonment was not at all unusual for a repentant prisoner, for the purpose was to protect society from a dangerous person. Thus, though the trial was illegal and the evidence specious, the outwards forms of the Inquisition were followed, right down to the lighting of the faggots. Perhaps the saddest part of this affair, even more so than Joan's personal tragedy, was the usurpation by the state of the powers of the Church. Thus was the Church weakened for its eventual loss of unity in the Protestant Reformation.

2

John Huss lived in troubled times. He was a child when the Great Schism began, and he died before it was healed. The Great Schism refers to that period when there were three claimants to the papacy. It began in 1378, upon the death of Gregory XI. This pope was the last of the Avignon line, the pope who returned to Rome to end the "Babylonian Captivity." For seventy years the popes had remained away from Rome, living in Avignon, in southern France. During this time the French began to look upon the papacy as their own. At last, due in great part to the urgings of St. Catherine of Siena, Gregory returned to Rome, only to die one year later. The conclave held upon his death to elect a new pope chose a Neapolitan, Urban VI. Since the Roman people had gathered about the building where the conclave was held, the French cardinals claimed that they had been coerced. They fled to Naples where they elected another pope, Clement VII. For long years there were two popes, both excommunicating each other, both trying to collect church tithes, both trying to administer the church. The original claimants died and successors for each were elected, worsening the situation. A council met at Pisa in 1409 to resolve the situation. They only worsened it by electing a third pope, John XXIII, whom the other two immediately excommunicated, while he excommunicated them. Europe was torn by this split in the papacy, none being sure whether their sacraments were validly administered or whether they were giving allegiance to an anti-pope. This situation was not resolved until the Council of Constance, the same council that condemned John Huss to die at the stake.

John Huss was born in Bohemia about 1370. Bohemia was that section of the Holy Roman Empire which was to become modern Czechoslovakia. Feelings of nationalism were beginning to stir at this time and the Bohemians longed to be free from allegiance to the empire. They were different in national origins from the Germans, with a different language. They had their own king, Wenceslaus. The empire was always an amalgam of semi-independent kingdoms and dukedoms, and always there were movements toward freedom. When the emperor was in Italy, the northern local rulers revolted or refused to pay taxes; when the emperor returned north to quell the disturbances it was time for the Italian princes to rise up. At the time of Huss, the Bohemians were not in revolt, but they were asserting their culture and their distinctness. There was a great university at Prague which drew students from all over Europe. Huss received his bachelor of arts from this university in 1393, his master of theology in 1394, and his master of arts in 1396. He never took his doctorate, but he began teaching at the university in 1396. In the year 1400 he was ordained priest. Huss was appointed a preacher in a Prague church in 1402 where his sermons, fervent and fiery, soon made him the most popular preacher in Bohemia. The people of Prague were fond of sermons, oddly enough, the longer the better. A good preacher drew large crowds. The faithful flocked to hear this new preacher, both because of his eloquence and because of subject matter. Huss caused a stir by demanding a purified church, one that exteriorly witnessed to its inner sanctity.

John Huss was deeply influenced by an English theologian, later denounced as a heretic, John Wycliffe. Wycliffe is often credited with introducing an English translation of the Bible, but this is not certain. His writings and thought were exported to Bohemia when Anne, the sister of King Wenceslaus married King Richard II of England. The increased contact between these two peoples soon brought Wycliffe's writings into the hands of Huss. The Englishman taught that the sins of popes, bishops, and priests rendered them unworthy of obedience. The Church, he said, should be poor, deprived of all its property. Its ministers should earn their living by working at an honorable trade. So far, he was in error only in the first proposition, that personal holiness was a requisite for the right to rule or administer the sacraments. The rest of his teachings were not heretical, expressing only a desire for a purified church. He erred from orthodoxy grievously, however, in his teachings about the Holy Eucharist. Wycliffe denied the doctrine of transubstantiation, which states that when bread and wine are consecrated only their appearance remains, their substance becoming the body and blood of Christ. For this doctrine he substituted a teaching called "remanance," which said that the substance of bread and wine co-existed with the substance of Christ. He also taught that the Bible, uninterpreted by the Church or by theologians, gave to the faithful a simple and unerring plan of salvation. This, too, was against orthodoxy. Huss never adopted Wycliffe's views on the Eucharist, but his other teachings were so similar to Wycliffe's that he was always accused of erring in his teachings on this point too. It was this confusion that eventually brought his death.

There is much in Wycliffe's and Huss's teachings that were of value. Truly, they desired a purified church, freed of the abuses that were then troubling it. They wanted the lives of the clergy to be worthy of their calling; they desired that the papacy be a spiritual force instead of dabbling in the unpleasant struggle for power, domains, and wealth. The abuses were real enough, as the Council of Trent later admitted. It was easier to condemn the excesses of these men than to go about the hard task of rooting out the faults that had grown cancerously on the human element of the Church. Yet, it is also true that Wycliffe strayed far from orthodoxy, and Huss fell into excess. Both men were led to over-state their case and react more vigorously than was necessary. In an age that valued orthodoxy this compromised their message of reform that was so important.

Wycliffe's writings were examined several times by Rome. They were condemned first in 1403, and once again in 1408. In 1410 the archbishop of Prague gathered together all the books of Wycliffe he could find and solemnly and publicly burned them. This was not sufficient to suppress the ideas the books expressed, for even as the books burned the people laughed that the archbishop was burning books he could not read. For all this, Wycliffe was never disturbed nor persecuted, for he had strong defenders among the rulers and the power of the papacy was weakened by the Great Schism. He managed to grow old and die peacefully in his own bed. John Huss, however, was now treading on dangerous ground.

Though he did not subscribe to all of Wycliffe's teachings, rejecting especially his doctrines on the Eucharist, he was constantly accused of being a heretic. The common people adopted his teachings and looked upon him as a prophet of Bohemia. The barons and dukes of the country supported him, both from conviction and as a political tool. They used him as a rallying point of nationalism, as a weapon against a powerful clergy, and as an irritant to Sigismund, the Holy Roman Emperor. Bishops, abbots, and priors, motivated by both noble and ignoble reasons, condemned him roundly and denounced him to Rome. In 1411 he was excommunicated as a Wyckliffian heretic. He had enough popular support, however, to continue preaching without fear of reprisals, and indeed, his own archbishop supported him. Huss became important throughout Europe when a nationalistic struggle broke out between the German and Bohemian students at the University of Prague. At last the German students withdrew and founded the University of Leipsig. They carried with them the report that Bohemia was honeycombed with heresy and John Huss was the leader. Even when a new archbishop, Conrad, came to Prague in 1413, endorsing Huss's views and positions, the outcry went on.

In 1414 both Emperor Sigismund and the Pisan anti-pope, John XXIII, summoned the Council of Constance. The announced purpose of this council was the healing of the Great Schism, stamping out heresy, and reforming the Church. To it came not only the bishops and high ecclesiastics, but also the major rulers of Europe. Since all Europe was clamoring about John Huss, both the pope and the emperor wished him to appear before the council to defend his views. Huss could have remained in Bohemia and been safe under the protection of the nobles. Instead, he began immediately to prepare for the journey, taking certain safeguards first. He received from his archbishop a letter stating his orthodoxy, and also got a similar document from the inquisitor of Prague. He sent friends to Sigismund to get a letter of safe-conduct, guaranteeing his freedom and his right to return to Prague. In this, he sadly underestimated his enemies. He was a doomed man as soon as he entered the city of Constance. His reputation had preceded him, and people stared at him as a curiosity. He aroused hostility by celebrating Mass even though he was under a sentence of excommunication. His enemies watched over him constantly even though he was treated civilly during the early part of his stay in the city.

Was John Huss a heretic? This is a difficult question to answer. Certainly men used his teachings to put forward unorthodox ideas. Certainly he was erroneous in not recognizing the teaching authority of the Church. Obviously he was falsely accused of denying the doctrine of transubstantiation and of teaching that the sacraments were worthless when administered by sinful hands. That these two charges were used against him is proof of the ill-will and unscrupulosity of his accusers, who were willing to do anything to obtain the destruction of their enemy. Huss repeatedly stated that he was willing to abide by any declaration of the council, but this brought him no safety. It is true that he made the work of his enemies easier by his imprudent actions at the council and by his argumentative nature. He seemed not to understand his danger, and when the trap was closed on him he seemed eager for martyrdom.

The enemies of Huss drew up a set of formal charges against him, based mainly on his own writings. These were presented to the council which now entered upon an inquisitorial process of examining him. According to the usual custom, John XXIII had Huss imprisoned while the examination went on. The council appointed a commission which acted as inquisitors, while the council itself served as a board of assessors. Several times Huss was brought before the commission for questioning. The charges were read to him at the first session. He was accused of denying transubstation, of denying the effectiveness of the sacraments in sinful hands, of defending the condemned teachings of Wycliffe, and of turning the people against the clergy. He was asked if he would defend these theses. Huss refused, saying he would accept the council's decisions. This was looked upon as mere evasion. In the inquisitorial process penitence was proved only by admitting and abjuring heresy. Huss admitted some of the charges placed against him, others he denied, and others he accepted with explanations. In all, he defended himself brilliantly. The inquisitorial process was somewhat relaxed in his favor. He was permitted on three occasions to address the council to explain his teachings. He was even permitted to examine some of the witnesses. He would not, however, budge from his position that he would submit to the council. Under no conditions would he admit heresy or abjure. He maintained to the end that the charges against him contained lies, and it seems this charge is true.

In July, 1415, the council heard the commission and judged Huss guilty of heresy. It decreed that he was to be given over to the secular arm if he did not repent. On two occasions his friends and the commissioners sought to find a compromise, for the council did not wish to make Huss a martyr. All came to naught when a final attempt was made on July 5. The next day, July 6, 1415, John Huss was taken to the stake and burned. His ashes were thrown into the Rhine. Huss was a victim of nationalism, of the struggle between church and emperor, of abuses within the church. The Council of Constance did heal the Great Schism, but it is stained by the death of Huss. It has been proposed several times that the name of Huss be cleared, as was Joan of Arc's. To date, nothing has come of these suggestions.

Joan of Arc: at the Siege of Orleans, 1429. Painting by Lenepveu.

The Trial of Joan of Arc. Painting by Frederick Rae.

Galileo (1564-1642) Italian Astronomer and Physicist Being Tried
by the Church. Engraving.

3

The Catholic Church has suffered much because of the Galileo case. For centuries her enemies have used this unfortunate affair in an attempt to show that the Church is a reactionary body opposed to science, truth, and freedom. The institutional Church was in fault enough to give later Catholics a cause for regret. Yet, both Galileo and the Church were, in a way, common victims of at least two hostile forces. The first force was a phenomenal growth in knowledge that expanded faster than society could absorb and adapt to it. The shock of the new understanding of the universe challenged not only the Church, but also the faculties of all the universities and the common man in the street. Galileo and the Church were caught in this turmoil. The second force was the enormous powers of the religious orders, especially the Dominicans and the Jesuits. These two orders, which were operating as a state within a state, a church within a church, were locked in a rivalry for power and preeminence. The Dominicans had lately won a subtle theological war based on a question of man's free will and the grace of God. The Jesuits were determined to lose no more battles. In the course of this struggle both Galileo and the Church were victimized by a forged document. It was this document that served as the basis of Galileo's condemnation.

Galileo worked under the patronage of the Medicis in Florence. It was early in the 1600's, when the Renaissance was drawing to a close. In the course of his work on mechanics he came across the telescope, just recently discovered, and constructed a good, powerful instrument of his own that was superior to the toys then in use. With his telescope he was able to see that the moon was mountainous, that Venus had phases, and Jupiter had moons. He also observed the spots on the sun and the rings of Saturn. Galileo used all these discoveries to bolster and further the Copernican theory of the universe. Copernicus, who had died in 1543, had demonstrated that the sun was the center of our planetary system, while the planets revolved about it. This idea was not totally unknown, even in ancient Greece, but astronomers had adopted the Ptolomaic system, in which the earth was the stationary center of the universe around which moved the moon, planets, sun, and stars. Aristotle, the supreme authority of the medieval universities, taught the same thing.

We find it hard to believe that the Copernican theory could stir up so much hatred and opposition. At the time of Galileo, however, there were two forces at work. The first was the universities. Aristotle was regarded as having all truth. To settle any argument it was sufficient to quote the master. If Aristotle was wrong in his theory of the universe, he might be wrong in any of his other positions. Then the entire structure of learning was brought in question. Learned doctors made their living and their reputations interpreting Aristotle. They had a vested interest in upholding the smallest of his statements. Such men could not help seeing Galileo as a threat to their entire lives. He was a man to be fought with any weapon and beaten by any means. The second force was no less implacable. Theologians saw a threat to the Holy Scriptures in the Copernican theory. There were many biblical texts that take for granted that the sun moves about the earth. The most classical instance is Joshua's stopping the course of the sun until the Israelites finished a battle. If scripture were proven wrong in this, they thought, the entire sub-structure of theology was wiped out. Galileo pointed out that the Bible was not a book of science. Its concern was revealing God to man in terms man could understand. All statements about the moving of the sun or the stability of the earth could be treated metaphorically without harming the inspired word of God. This is exactly how we interpret scripture today, based on our greater understanding of biblical theology. The learned men of Galileo's time regarded this as a dangerous idea.

Much of the difficulty that Galileo experienced came about because men had confused and merged theology and science. Theology was the "queen of the sciences," encompassing all the rest. A scientist could not study ants, much less the universe, without becoming involved in theology. Just as the Church suffered because of the confusion between the power of Church and state, so the Church suffered because of the confusion between theology and the other sciences. This idea of the universe put forward by Copernicus and championed by such men as Galileo, Kepler, and Tycho Brahe was purely scientific, based upon observation and mathematical calculations. The proof was purely scientific, and the scientists should not have been forced to become theologians also. What was necessary was a re-thinking of theology, to see if what was being taught as God's revelation was indeed such. Perhaps the best thing that could have happened would have been the summoning of a Church council to examine the doctrine of the universe. Cardinal Newman has pointed out that the dogmas of the Church are capable of developing and unfolding. While God has finished his revelation in the Bible, he says, man's understanding of that revelation is capable of growing constantly. Galileo lived at a time when doctrine should have expanded in the light of the new discoveries, and a general council was the best place to bring about this development. Two popes, however, Paul V and Urban VIII, chose to deal with the new teachings as administrative matters. In such a procedure Galileo was doomed.

In 1615 Galileo was denounced to the Holy Office by a Dominican friar of little learning, Thomas Caccini. His accusation was that Galileo was teaching contrary to the scriptures. He used as part of his evidence a letter that Galileo had written. This letter, however, had been altered by another friar, named Lorini, in two vital spots. This false evidence started the case against Galileo, who was summoned to Rome for a hearing. In 1616 Cardinal Robert Bellarmine, the head of the Holy Office and the man in charge of the Inquisition, suspended the writings of Copernicus until they should be corrected. Both Bellarmine and Pope Paul V warned Galileo that while he was free to express the Copernican ideas he could do so only if he presented them as theories, not as facts. Church authorities were unwilling to condemn the new ideas, but they were also unwilling to see them expounded as actual fact. In other words, these men were unwilling to settle the theological problems involved.

Galileo departed from Rome in 1616 loaded with honors and with a letter from Cardinal Robert Bellarmine stating that Galileo had not been found guilty of anything, had not been punished, and had not withdrawn any of his ideas. However, skullduggery was being performed in the Holy Office itself. Some official added on a note to the words of Cardinal Bellarmine, stating that Galileo had been ordered not to hold nor to teach the idea that the earth moved about the sun. The entire file of the Galileo case as found in the offices of the Inquisition was published in 1877. From both internal evidence and from a study of history scholars have concluded that an enemy of Galileo had inserted into the file a false document, for it is clear that Galileo had received no warning against holding or teaching the Copernican ideas. Yet that document served as the basis for his condemnation seventeen years later.

In 1616, then, Galileo returned to Florence and to work, with no knowledge that a time bomb had been planted in his files in the Inquisition offices. He continued to work on the mathematical underpinnings of the Copernican theory, bolstered by his own astronomical observations. Galileo was not right in all his theorizing. He never grasped the fact that the planets moved in an elliptical orbit. His holding to the idea of circular orbits led to several false conclusions. Likewise, he tried to explain tides by saying they were the effect of the turning of the earth on its axis. Unfortunately Isaac Newton was not to be born until 1642 and Galileo needed the Englishman's understanding of gravity and the laws of motion to complete his own work. He continued living the scientist's life in peace and quiet, but his enemies were not resting. Several pieces of Galileo's writings kept their fury burning while they awaited their opportunity. It came when Galileo decided to write his great work, *The Dialogue of the Chief World Systems*. Renaissance man that he was, he was not content with the dry scientific writing intended only for experts that we are familiar with today. He composed his scientific tract in the form of literature, a conversation between four people who represented different views of the universe. Each presented his views, which were discussed by the others. Galileo hoped that this method would meet the restrictions placed upon him by Paul V and Urban VIII, who demanded that the ideas be put forward only as theories, not as established fact. Upon completing his work he had difficulty getting ecclesiastical permission to publish the book. The examination dragged along in Rome so long that eventually Galileo submitted the text to the inquisitor at Florence, who suggested some changes and then gave a license for the publication of the *Dialogue*. The book was written in Italian, the vernacular tongue rather than the scholarly Latin which could be read only by a few. The book was an instant success, every copy being snapped up by scholars and by the educated people who were interested in the new learning. The book was published in 1632.

Galileo's enemies now began furious activity. He and his book were bitterly denounced in Rome. He was accused of outright heresy, of violating the restrictions of the popes, of ignoring Bellarmine's "warning" (which had never been given), of fomenting trouble by writing in Italian. In short order he was summoned to Rome to undergo questioning. The order came directly from Pope Urban VIII, long-time friend and admirer of Galileo, who nevertheless saw a danger to the Faith just at the time when the Church was still struggling with the effects of Protestantism. Galileo, now sixty-nine years old, left in mid-winter, on February 16, for the Holy City. Even as he traveled he was sure that nothing could happen to him, for he was equipped with the letter from Cardinal Bellarmine and the personal assurances of the Pope. He was unaware that the false notation in the Holy Office was waiting to accuse him, nor that the Pope and his highest advisers had determined to stamp out Copernican speculation. Galileo was first interrogated by a panel of ten inquisitors, all cardinals of the Church, on April 12, 1633. There he first learned of the planted evidence. Even then, he thought Bellarmine's letter was enough to give him security.

His fate, however, was sealed. The board of experts, the assessors common to all inquisitions, decreed on June 16 that Galileo was guilty of "vehement suspicion of heresy." It was charged that he violated the injunction of 1616 "not to hold or teach" that the earth moved. Further, it was charged that he had obtained his license to publish the *Dialogue* by fraud, since he had not told the examiners about the injunction of 1616. He was accused of going against the sense of Scripture in his ideas and writings. It was not the Church which so decreed, but a group of ten cardinals and their aides. While this frees the Church of any suspicion of false doctrine it does not free the institutional Church of rashness and injustice. These men, who acted in the name of the Church, could not claim the charity of Christ, nor of having God's interests uppermost in their hearts. The pilgrim Church, as it moves through history, is constantly purifying itself so that it will more truly show forth its Master and Lord. While we might hope and expect that human rights and freedom should be respected by that body which claims to be divine as well as human we should not be surprised that the human often prevails. We should also remember that this was the time of general intrigue throughout Europe, and the Borgias had only recently ceased their infamous activities. In the North, Protestantism was persecuting its scientists, too.

On June 21, 1633, the decree aaginst him was read to Galileo and he was ordered to recant. Always the faithful Catholic, he did so in a form that saved his honor and left him free to believe as the evidence he saw dictated he must. He was sentenced to imprisonment but the pope commuted this to house arrest at his estate at Arcetri. There he spent his last years, continuing his work even after he became blind in 1637. He published other writings after this time, though they had to be taken out of Italy to be printed. He was visited by many learned men from all over the world and had the pleasure of holding in his hands an English translation of the *Dialogue*. He died in 1642, shortly before his seventy-eighth birthday.

The Galileo case had several unfortunate results. It has served as a weapon to use against the Church by her enemies, even few of them bother trying to understand how complex the case actually was, and how much it depended on a false document. This one case also helped establish a false war between religion and science. It was Galileo himself who wrote that the God who speaks in the books of the Bible also speaks in the book of nature, and he is not likely to contradict himself. Scientific investigation received a severe setback in Italy, which had been as advanced in science as it had been in art. All things considered, the Galileo affair can only be regarded as unmitigated tragedy.

5

The Spanish Inquisition

THE SPANISH INQUISITION DESERVES special treatment, for it is quite different from the papal Inquisition of the Middle Ages. While its organization was much the same as the medieval Inquisition it served quite different ends. The Spanish Inquisition was established by the king and queen of Spain and remained dependent upon the crown throughout its long existence. The inquisitors were appointed by the king and served at his will and discretion. The Spanish Inquisition was not established until the medieval Inquisition was well past its prime. It continued to endure, in a weakened state, until the nineteenth century. It differed from its medieval counterpart by becoming centralized. The central agency became known as the *Suprema* and in time the local inquisitors forwarded all their evidence to it. It was the *Suprema* which evaluated the evidence and passed sentence. The Spanish Inquisition is also noted as having raised the *sermo generalis,* known in Spain as the *auto de fe,* into an art form.

The very name of the Spanish Inquisition is taken today as a synonym for terror and cruelty. The first Inquisitor-General, Thomas Torquemada, is infamous in legend as a ruthless persecutor and heartless torturer. Neither reputation is deserved. The Spanish Inquisition was kinder and more lenient than civil courts in either Spain or the rest of Europe. Its victims were no more numerous than those acts of insanity that broke out in France (the St. Bartholomew's Day Massacre), or in Germany, or in the Netherlands. The beheadings, the hangings, the drawing and quareterings of Henry VIII far surpassed the cruelty of the Spanish Inquisition. The persecution of Catholics under Queen Elizabeth I was more ruthless than anything Spain had known. Both the Spanish Inquisition and Torquemada got their bad reputation from the political quarrel that arose when the Netherlands strove for independence from the Spanish king, Philip V. The Protestant Netherlands used every weapon, including religious bigotry which was everywhere present at that time, to gain their national freedom. Most of the legends of the cruelty of the Spanish Inquisition spring from this time. The secrecy under which the Inquisition always operated gave such legends a ring of truth and made refuting them very difficult. Compared to the atrocities we have seen in our own day the Spanish Inquisition has a kind of innocence. We need only think of prisoners in Russian courts standing up to accuse themselves of crimes against the state, knowing that the death that would follow was preferable to the torture claims of innocence brought. We need only recall how Cardinal Mindszenty was brought to confess his "crimes" against Hungary. After the Korean War we found that many United States prisoners-of-war had been subjected to brainwashing. We need only recall how when the American ship, *Pueblo*, was captured by North Korea, the captain, and then crew, were quickly brought to a "confession." In our own country it is not unknown that men have been convicted of crimes on the basis of confessions extorted under torture, though happily these seem few. The Spanish Inquisition never reached the savagery of any of these cases. Its basic error was the error common to those times, an attempt at thought control, a desire to wipe out an idea by punishing its proponents rather than by refuting it. This error is not unknown in our recent history. Fortunately, we are largely protected by law.

The papal Inquisition of the Middle Ages never gained a foothold in Spain. At that time the country was divided into two main kingdoms, the northern Kingdom of Aragon and the larger kingdom of Castile. Both were concerned with driving off the Moors who conquered much of the Spanish peninsula. For this reason, feudalism was never a Spanish institution as it was in the remainder of Europe. The ordinary people of Spain always regarded themselves as good as any noble of the blood royal. The Albigenses were never numerous in the northern kingdom, and all but unknown in Castile. The institution of the Inquisition was regarded as so peculiarly a Catholic symbol that several attempts were made to establish it in Aragon. In 1238 an inquisitor operated in Aragon, and in 1242 a Council of Tarragona, established guidelines for an Inquisition, headed by St. Raymond of Pennaforte. No Inquisition in Spain was ever very powerful, and none had much work to do.

The Spanish Inquisition came into being under their "Catholic Majesties," Ferdinand and Isabella. In 1469 Ferdinand, known as "the Catholic," married Isabella. Ferdinand was the heir to the throne of Aragon, while Isabella was heir to the throne of Castile. In 1474 Isabella took her place as queen of the larger kingdom and Ferdinand acceded to the throne of Aragon in 1479. From this time a unified Spain became a fact. Though each kingdom for a time kept its own constitutions and assemblies, the kingdoms were in fact united under the heir of the two monarchs. At this time the re-conquest of Spain from the Moors was nearing completion.

Many of the Moors who had lived in the reclaimed territories wished to live in the only land they had ever known. A large number of them became Catholics while still keeping their own culture. In the cities, the middle class was made up almost entirely of Jews. They were the merchants, the doctors, the lawyers, the bankers. They were what we would call today "the entrepreneurs" of Spain. The nobles owned huge areas of land which they farmed and grazed, while the peasants owned their small farms.

Now, a peculiar idea arose in Spain. It was known as *limpieza,* or "racial purity." We know what horrors this concept can bring from our experience with Hitler. It did not reach the madness of Nazism in Spain, but it did bear its usual evil fruit. This concept was reinforced by economic considerations and religious overtones. The Moors and the Jews were by far wealthier than the ordinary Spaniard, and indeed than most of the nobility, who were land-poor. By moving against these two classes the crown and the nobles would have access to their wealth. The crown would have another weapon aaginst the towns, whose independent power was a threat to its power. The religious overtone was one common to all of Europe. A nation of one religion was easier to rule than a nation in which many beliefs flourished. Added to this was an anti-semitism that was all too common and which the Second Vatican Council was later to deplore: "The Church repudiates all persecutions against any man. Moreover, mindful of her common patrimony with the Jews and motivated by the gospel's spiritual love and by no political considerations, she deplores the hatred, persecutions, and displays of anti-Semitism directed against the Jews at any time and from any source. Besides, as the Church has always held and continues to hold, Christ in his boundless love freely underwent His passion and death because of the sins of all men, so that all might attain salvation."

As early as 1391 many Jews were forced to accept baptism or face death. In 1412 the Jews were ordered to wear yellow badges, four fingers in length, upon their hearts. (The Nazis later followed a similar policy.) The Cortes, or assembly, held at Toledo in 1480 re-confirmed this legislation. On March 31, 1492, all Jews were ordered to leave Spain. About 200,000 fled the country in which they had been born and in which they had deep roots and ancient ancestry. They went to France, to the Netherlands, to Italy, leaving behind almost everything they owned. They were forbidden by law to remove any gold from Spain. Rather than face an exile from a land which they naturally regarded as their own, perhaps 50,000 accepted baptism. Even this did not bring them full acceptance, for converts from Islam and the Jews were known as *conversos,* or New Christians. The rest referred to themselves as Old Christians. Many of the conversos became Christians in name only. While outwardly they practiced their Christian religion, in private they maintained their Jewish beliefs and customs. Even those who were sincere converts found it difficult to lay aside their Jewishness entirely. It was a way of life for them. They could not, for instance, bring themselves to eat pork. Surely no man should be forced to eat what he does not wish to eat, but even so minor a detail might bring ruin to a converso.

Because feudalism had never had a place in Spain it was possible for a man to move up the social ladder according to his abilities. The conversos intermarried with even the nobility and soon were holding high offices even in the Church. Torquemada, for example, came from a converso family, as did St. Teresa of Avila and St. John of the Cross. Some even claim that Columbus came from a converso family, and certainly many of his crew were conversos. Ecclesiastical authorities panicked at the thought of the many false Christians. They did not reflect how unfair it was to offer a man a choice of giving up his religious beliefs or accepting exile or death. Instead, they clamored for an Inquisition to search out "judaizers," or conversos who secretly continued to practice the religion of their ancestors. At the appeal of the bishops Pope Sixtus IV allowed Spain to have two Inquisitors, to be appointed by the crown. In 1480 two Dominicans were appointed, who immediately went to work in Seville. It is important to realize that the Inquisition had power only over the baptized. About 4000 conversos immediately fled the city. The first auto de fe was celebrated on February 6, 1481 at which six conversos were burned at the stake. In the first eight years of the Seville Inquisition over 700 persons were burned and over 5000 punished.

In 1482 seven more inquisitors were appointed, among them Thomas Torquemada. These men set up tribunals in the main cities of the peninsula. In 1483 a Supreme Council for the Inquisition was established by the crown, headed by an Inquisitor-General, who was Torquemada. This council later came to be known simply as the Suprema. As for Torquemada, he simply did what he was supposed to do under the laws. During the time that he was Inquisitor-General perhaps 2000 were sent to the stake. He was responsible for the death of about half of these. It is a grim record, but no one of the time regarded him as cruel. The legends of his iniquities did not arise until a full century later. As for this Inquisition, it was established by the crown, that is, by Ferdinand and Isabella. The popes tried several times to interfere but the rulers persisted in their ways. Once the pope remonstrated that the persecution of the conversos was based on nothing more than a desire for their wealth, but nothing came of his protestation. Having engaged in secular power politics, the papacy was in no position to exercise a spiritual dominance. The Inquisition gained popular support in 1485 when Peter, the inquisitor at Saragossa, was assassinated while at prayer in the cathedral. The murderers were quickly caught. It developed that they had been hired by conversos who saw in the inquisitor a threat to their safety. This one deed stirred up the people to such a degree that the Inquisition was given all the impetus it needed for full establishment. In 1486 Pope Innocent VIII revoked all independent papal inquisitors, leaving the Spanish Inquisition supreme. (In the nineteenth century Peter was canonized as a saint. He is sometimes known as St. Peter Martyr, not to be confused with another St. Peter Martyr, who was an inquisitor in Italy and slain in 1252. There are many cases of the persecuted finally turning in desperation and killing the inquisitors.)

The procedure of the Spanish Inquisition was generally the same as that of the medieval Inquisition. All deeds of the Inquisition were wrapped in the deepest secrecy. The purpose of the Inquisition was not to seek the ruin of heretics, but to discover them and reconcile them with the Church if possible. The establishment of the court in a locality as always began with a period of grace when heretics could denounce themselves and escape with light penalties. This seemed to work more effectively in Spain than in other places, for in one case more than three hundred came forward. The main interest of the Spanish Inquisition was "judaizers," or conversos who secretly practiced Judaism. When the Inquisition began operating in a locality it announced to the people the signs by which heretics and judaizers could be recognized: not eating pork, avoiding certain foods, keeping the Sabbath, saying the psalms without the Gloria Patri, and a host of other signs. When the period of grace was past the court began to take evidence and summon the accused. The Spanish Inquisition differed from other Inquisitions in that it allowed the accused a defense lawyer. This lawyer, however, could not cross-examine witnesses or even know the specific charges laid against his client. He could only bring forward whatever favorable evidence he could gather and then hope for the best. When at length a case was completed, the evidence was assessed. At first there was the usual board of assessors, but soon all cases were forwarded to the Suprema for assessment, judgment and sentence.

A large number of sentences were available to the Inquisition. Most cases ended in a reconciliation with the Church and the imposition of a penance more or less severe according to the offense. As was usual, confiscation of goods almost always accompanied a sentence of guilty, even though other penalties might be light. A convicted heretic could be sentenced to imprisonment for a short time, or for life. He could be sentenced to wear a *sanbenito*, which was a piece of cloth that hung down in front and back, yellow in color, with diagonal St. Andrew crosses on each side. This corresponded to the yellow crosses worn upon the clothing of those convicted in the papal Inquisitions. It was, of course, a humiliating punishment. When the period assigned was over, the sanbenito was hung from the rafters of the parish church as a memory of the shame of its wearer. Scourging was also a possible sentence. Sometimes the guilty were assigned as rowers on the Spanish galleys, furnishing a cheap supply of labor. Exile was a common punishment. Acquittals were not unknown in the Spanish Inquisition. Prosecutions that obviously had no basis were also disposed of by the face-saving device of dismissing the charge, or suspending the trial. During a thirty-five year period the Inquisition at Toledo turned over only fifteen persons to the secular arm, while reconciling 207, acquitting 51, and dismissing or suspending the cases against 128. These figures indicate that the Spanish Inquisition was not the monster of cruelty so often represented.

The secrecy of the Inquisition ended when the auto de fe was held. Contrary to popular opinion, executions had no part in the auto and were always held separately from it, and in a different place. The purpose of the ceremony was to reconcile the guilty wth the Church, while at the same time demonstrating to the populace the folly of heresy. In time it grew to be of huge size, long duration, and great solemnity. When the day of an auto de fe arrived the prisoners were prepared for the event. Those who were to be relaxed to the secular arm were clothed in a *sanbenito* decorated with flames and dancing demons. The condemned also wore a very tall, pointed cap on which the same designs appeared. A cross-bearer led the procession from the Inquisition offices to a nearby church where Mass was celebrated. Afterwards, the procession moved to the point where the ceremony was to take place. The ordinary penitents went first, followed by those who were to be given over to be burned at the stake, and last of all the glittering array of ecclesiastical and secular dignities. (Many times the auto was held in the presence of the king himself.) In a square high platforms had been constructed, and on these were civil authorities, nobles and ecclesiastics, and, on a separate platform, those whose sentence would be pronounced. The inquisitors and the preacher shared a smaller platform. A long, fervid sermon was always a part of the auto de fe, much enjoyed by the large numbers who turned out to watch the pageantry or to indulge their morbid curiosity. After the sermon the sentences of the penitents were read, one at a time. Since some ceremonies disposed of the cases of more than seven hundred penitents, this was a lengthy business, one which grew even lengthier with the passage of the years. It was not unusual for an auto de fe to last from dawn until well after the sun had set, the ceremony continuing amid the flickering of torches. The ceremony closed with the handing over to secular authorities those who refused reconciliation. These were taken to another place for the execution of the usual sentence. It was not uncommon for the executioner to strangle the victim before lighting the faggots of the pyre. Perhaps we wonder why men and women, knowing that they faced death after the ceremony kept their silence while all this took place. Most complied with the ceremonial requirements because they wished to maintain their dignity and avoid harsher punishments. Some did cry out and blaspheme. These were restrained by the use of whatever force was necessary.

As the years passed the Spanish Inquisition became more and more ineffective. It was subject to all sorts of abuses because of its close alliance with the civil power who used it to beat down opposition. Eventually it was a sad remnant of itself, reduced mainly to condemning books. On July 15, 1834, during the midst of an upheaval in Spanish life, a royal decree officially ended the life of an institution that had been effectively dead for a long time.

The Spanish Inquisition was unfortunate. How many died, no one can know. As an instrument of thought control it worked better than most, for the Protestant Reformation never took a foothold in Spain. It had the effect, however, of cutting off Spain from the intellectual life of Europe and driving from its borders the most liberal and energetic of its peoples. Many of the problems that it covered up have risen to meet modern Spain. While indefensible, the Spanish Inquisition was not the monster of iniquity it is often represented as being. Its sins were Spanish sins, not English sins, or French sins, or German or Dutch sins, and for this many people refuse to forgive it even as they absolve themselves.

6

Conclusions

IN SUCH A SHORT SURVEY of the Inquisition it has not been possible to cover all the fields in which it was active. It is not even desirable to do so, since an exhaustive study would obscure the more important outlines in which we are interested. It must be mentioned, however, that the Inquisition was not interested only in the Waldenses and the Albigenses. It dealt with all forms of heresy that occurred in the territories within which it operated. It effectively wiped out a heresy known as the "Spiritual Franciscans." It was responsible for the dissolution of the Knights Templar, a religious order made up of knights who had fought in the crusades and later guarded the Holy Land. Most interesting, perhaps, was the fight it waged against witchcraft. Late in the Middle Ages Europe lost its head on the subject of witches. Scores were burned as witches in all countries, including those in which the Inquisition was unknown. Old women were sent to the stake simply because a neighbor's child had grown sick or a sheep had died. The belief in witches was almost universal and the Inquisition busied itself with ferreting out and punishing those who practiced magic arts, and even those who were simply suspected of doing so. The fever did not escape America, for we remember that witches were burned in Salem.

A study of the Inquisition shows that it was not the horror it is usually imagined to be. Its sins were the sins of the times in which it operated. Compared to the civil courts it comes off well. Whatever cruelties it perpetrated were common to all courts of the time. We often err by judging the Inquisition apart from its times. Most of the inquisitors were just and honest men who believed in the rightness of their actions. The idea that men should not be persecuted for what they thought and believed had not been born in Europe in their time. The Inquisition cannot be blamed for operating on the concepts of its times. "Thought control" of the most flagrant kind is practiced in our own day in more than half of the world. Even in the United States the military draft laws do not permit a man to qualify as a conscientious objector because he considers the war he is being asked to fight as immoral. He can qualify as an objector only if he is opposed to the idea of all war. This is surely an infringement of man's freedom and a violation of the sanctity of his convictions. If we are able to be scandalized at the Inquisition it must be because it was an arm of the Church, which should have abhorred all force and shuned bringing death to any person. It is unfortunate that the Church ever fell into this trap and it has paid dearly for the slip.

A study of the Inquisition shows that it was a greater influence upon history than is generally credited. It greatly harmed the Church that instituted it, for most heresies were either a revolt against abuses within the Church or were signs that the Church was not doing its job. The Waldenses, for instance, arose as a protest against riches and worldliness. The Albigenses grew so rapidly because bishops neglected to teach and preach, leaving the people in ignorance, an easy prey for heretical doctrine. If the Church had regarded these heresies as symptoms of a disease within itself it could have purified and strengthened itself centuries before the Protestant Reformation forced it to do so. Instead, it regarded the symptoms as the disease itself and set out to eradicate them. The effects of this course of action are still present to the Church today, both within and without. The Inquisition also influenced history even by its negative attitude. Eventually it wiped out the Albigenses, holders of a dangerous and pernicious doctrine. It also undoubtedly left long-lasting effects upon certain localities. We have seen how the Inquisition affected the economic growth of southern France and all of Spain. Other countries, such as England or the Netherlands, profited from this flow of money and enterprising men. In these ways and many others more subtle the Inquisition deeply affected the course of European history.

The basic evil of the Inquisition was that it violated the sacred sanctuary of a man's thoughts and conscience. Some things cannot be commanded nor forbidden except for the survival of society itself. The United States does not forbid a man to believe in anarchy or communism, or anything else, for that matter. He comes under the sanctions of the law only if he urges the establishment of his system by the overthrow of the government by the use of force. A man is free to urge his fellow-citizens to adopt a communistic form of government, since our laws recognize his right to think or advocate whatever he wishes, short of force. The line is drawn at the use of force or advocating the use of force. The Inquisition refused to accept the idea that a person's intellect could not be coerced, and from this flowed all its practices and policies.

The Church has forever abandoned the idea of thought control. This was true for long years before the Second Vatican Council specifically stated that force should not be used to make a person change his beliefs. Any institution should have enough faith in its doctrines to believe that it can succeed through argument and persuasion. It has taken long, however, for this concept to become part of our civilization. It had no place in the intellectual or moral armories of the Middle Ages, nor in any previous age. We should not be surprised, therefore, that the Inquisition acted in accordance with the thinking of its times.

The Inquisition has long disappeared from the scene, yet its reputation remains behind. That reputation is often distorted and falsified, seen out of historical context. We have arrived at a stage of our human development where we should be concerned with forgiveness and reconciliation, not with perpetuating old grievances and misunderstandings. For this reason it is important that we have an understanding of the Inquisition, both in its unfortunate aspects and in its historical inevitability. Seen in a clear perspective we are able to understand; understanding, we can forgive; forgiving, we can place it behind and move onward in the march of civilization.